The Urge to Punish

BOOKS BY HENRY WEIHOFEN

Mental Disorder as a Criminal Defense

Psychiatry and the Law (*with Manfred S. Guttmacher*)

May's Criminal Law, 4th Edition
(*with Kenneth C. Sears*)

Insanity as a Defense in Criminal Law

THE ISAAC RAY AWARD BOOK

The Urge to Punish

NEW APPROACHES TO THE PROBLEM OF MENTAL IRRESPONSIBILITY FOR CRIME

HENRY WEIHOFEN

FARRAR, STRAUS AND CUDAHY

NEW YORK

Foreword

This book comprises the fourth annual Isaac Ray lectures, delivered at Temple University, Philadelphia, in December, 1955.

The American Psychiatric Association established the Isaac Ray Award in 1952, to be given annually to the person deemed "most worthy by reason of his contribution to the improvement of the relations of law and psychiatry." The awardee undertakes to deliver a series of lectures at some university having both a law school and a medical school, to be selected by the association's board in charge of the award. The first awardee was Dr. Winfred Overholser, superintendent of St. Elizabeth's Hospital, Washington, D. C., and past president of the American Psychiatric Association. The second was Dr. Gregory Zilboorg, author of *Mind, Medicine and Man,* and numerous other writings. The third was Judge John Biggs, Jr., Chief Judge of the United States Court of Appeals for the Third Judicial Circuit.

To be chosen to join this distinguished company is an honor that buoys the spirit, but it is also a responsibility of some magnitude. The ideal person to make a true contribution to the relations of law and psychiatry would be one who was master of both disciplines. I am a lawyer; I am not a psychiatrist. The best substitute I can offer for a collaboration of law and psychiatry under one skull is a discussion of certain problems in the area where law and psychiatry overlap, which may stimulate further thinking by members of both professions.

Rather than touch upon many subjects, I have preferred to discuss in some detail one specific and current
issue. That is the problem of how we should deal with
cases in which the question arises whether a person
charged with crime was so mentally disordered at the
time of the act charged that he should be held irresponsible. This is hardly a novel subject. It has dominated
most of the prior Isaac Ray lectures and has been the
subject of a vast amount of other writing. But it is more
timely today than ever, because after more than a century of almost complete immobility, the law seems suddenly to be stirring. Change is not merely being urged
by individual writers; it is being urged by agencies who
carry great weight, and who are almost certain to achieve
some action. What is more, some action has already been
had. It is these happenings that are examined and evalu-
ated in this book.

In delivering these and other lectures over the country, I have enjoyed the opportunity of discussing some
of the more crucial aspects of the problem with psychiatrists who are in the forefront of research and experimental activities now under way. To them I am much
indebted for giving me much fresh information. I am
particularly indebted for help on the psychiatric aspects
to my good friends, Dr. Manfred S. Guttmacher, Chief
Medical Officer of the Supreme Bench of Baltimore, and
Dr. Winfred Overholser, Superintendent of St. Elizabeth's Hospital, Washington, D. C.

H. W.

Contents

The Urge to Punish

CHAPTER ONE

Dr. Ray's Rule

Some years ago, a young man, a student at Franklin and Marshall College in Lancaster, Pennsylvania, was charged with the murder of a young woman who worked in the administrative offices of the college. He had known her only casually, and it was by mere chance that he happened to meet her that day on the street. He suggested a ride in his car. They rode out past the country club; he stopped the car, reached over and choked her to death.

At his trial for murder, there was evidence that he had a latent psychosis, schizophrenia; and that while he was perhaps not totally irresponsible, he did not possess sufficient or average capacity to understand the nature and quality of his act.

The law must have a rule or standard for determining whether such a person should be held "guilty" and punished as a criminal, or found "not guilty by reason of insanity" and committed to a mental institution for care and treatment. The use of the ambiguous word "insanity" leads to some confusion. The term is frequently used (by lawyers) to mean mental disorder or mental disease, and this sometimes leads to the assumption that mental disorder as such will relieve from criminal responsibility.[1] But that is not so, and cannot be so. There is no clear dichotomy between mental health and mental illness. The one shades by degrees into the other,[2] and the law therefore must of necessity draw a line demarking the degree or form of mental illness or the effects produced thereby, that will serve to render a person mentally irresponsible.

Our law has had extraordinary difficulty in tracing this line. The judges of England in 1843 undertook to restate the then existing law on the subject, and their successors, in England and in America, have in the main held staunchly to the "knowledge of right and wrong" test there laid down. But its interpretation and its application has not been easy. And critics have from the beginning questioned both its legal and its scientific soundness.

One of the earliest and one of the most effective of these critics was an American physician, Dr. Isaac Ray, whose voice was first heard when he was still a young practitioner in Eastport, Maine. It seems appropriate to devote these lectures in honor of Dr. Ray to an examination of the reform he advocated in the law governing mental disorder as a defense to a criminal charge, a reform that may prove to be the most lasting and most valuable of his many valuable contributions to the relations of law and psychiatry.

Beginning at least as early as 1838, in the work for which he is mainly remembered, *The Medical Jurispru-*

dence of Insanity, and throughout his long professional career, Dr. Ray opposed the existing legal tests of his day, which, as already indicated, remain essentially the existing tests of our day. These tests, he said, had their origins in an age when criminal procedure involved no use of expert witnesses, or even of counsel for the accused. The judge had to instruct the jury on medical facts, and the "tests" of insanity grew out of judicial efforts to supply the jury with such information, obtained from medical books.[3]

Then in later cases, the judges, following their penchant for precedent, took to repeating what they had said in the earlier case. And since now they were quoting from a case, it was easy to take the quoted medical statements as if they were statements of law. As such, they were cut off from their scientific source, and took on weight in themselves. Medical men abandoned the old ideas, new medical works replaced those that the original judges had dipped into, but the new judge didn't have to read the new scientific works. The old statement about mental disorder had become a proposition of law, and so of course invulnerable to new ideas of mere medical men.

Dr. Ray urged abolishing all such tests and substituting the simple rule that in criminal cases, insane persons should not be held responsible for their criminal acts unless the acts are proved not to have been the direct or indirect result of the insanity. The jury, he said, should be permitted to decide whether or not the mental disorder, if it existed, embraced the criminal act in its sphere of influence.[4]

In 1850, while serving as superintendent of the Butler Hospital in Providence, Rhode Island, Dr. Ray proposed a "Project of a Law for Regulating the Legal Relations of the Insane." In this proposal he discussed the civil liability of the mentally ill, advocated sending defendants to a mental hospital for a period of observation whenever a question arose of their mental fitness to stand trial, and in criminal cases urged the rule already mentioned. He submitted this idea for such a project to the Association of Medical Superintendents of American Institutions for the Insane, now the American Psychiatric Association, of which he had been one of the "Original Thirteen." After years of effort, he succeeded, in 1864, in getting the Association to adopt his project, including the proposed rule that insane persons should not be held responsible for criminal acts unless such acts be proved not to have been the result, directly or indirectly, of insanity. But neither Dr. Ray's books—authoritative as these were regarded by the courts—nor his various articles in medical and legal journals, nor the endorsement of the Association, seemed to be having any influence in inducing the courts to discard the existing tests of criminal insanity and substitute his proposed rule. In 1867 he resigned his position as superintendent of Butler Hospital, partly because of failing health, and moved to Philadelphia. He promptly interested himself in civic affairs, lectured for a time in one of the medical colleges, and continued to write on medico-legal matters.[5]

Shortly before coming to Philadelphia he had begun what turned out to be a most significant correspondence with Judge Charles Doe of the New Hampshire Supreme Court. Judge Doe was himself a rather remarkable man. Roscoe Pound included him among "the ten judges who must be ranked first in American judicial history."[6] This correspondence continued over six years. It has recently been unearthed and published by Dr. Louis E. Reik of Princeton, under the title, "The Doe-Ray Correspondence: A Pioneer Collaboration in the Jurisprudence of Mental Disease."[7]

It was indeed a "collaboration" and a very fruitful one, for it led to the adoption of Ray's view by the New Hampshire court. Doe started the correspondence when the court had before it a case involving mental capacity to make a will. The majority of the court approved instructions that told the jury delusions were the test of insanity. Judge Doe, influenced by the criticisms of the legal tests expressed in Ray's *Medical Jurisprudence,* determined to write a dissenting opinion. He wrote Ray about the case, asking for an expression of his views. Ray answered, and over the next six years the two exchanged at least twenty letters, in which they helped clarify each other's thinking. In his dissent in the will case, *Boardman* v. *Woodman,* decided in 1866,[8] Judge Doe insisted that whether delusion is a symptom or test of insanity is a question of fact and not of law, and that it was therefore error for the trial judge to charge the jury on the question as one of law.

Three years later, Judge Doe had brought Chief Justice Perley round to his view. In a criminal case in which Perley sat as trial judge, he adopted this view in charging the jury. "All symptoms and all tests of mental disease are purely matters of fact to be determined by the jury," he told them. If they found that the homicide was the product of the mental disease, they should find the defendant not guilty by reason of insanity. On appeal, this was upheld by the entire court, in an opinion written by Judge Doe.[9]

Judge Doe's next letter to Ray was exultant. "It is certain" he wrote, "that no such instructions were ever before given to a jury in England or America." He optimistically hoped the legal profession of the country could be induced to adopt the new rule, and outlined his strategy for bringing this about.

Ray was less sanguine. "This rule," he wrote Doe on January 12, 1869, "indicates a great advance beyond the usual practice — too great I fear to be generally accepted even in your generation [Doe was then thirty-eight years old; Ray was almost sixty- two]. However, we ought to be very thankful that it is likely to be adopted, shortly, in one state. I suppose it will finally be accepted everywhere, because I am sure it indicates the true spirit and genius of the law, and is in accordance with the temper and habits of our people."

Ray was the sounder prophet. The rule was reaffirmed

(and somewhat reformulated) by the New Hampshire Supreme Court in 1871,[10] but with that, it lost its impetus. Not only was it not adopted elsewhere; it was not even discussed. It was worse than rejected, it was ignored. Certain writers endorsed it from time to time, but the courts of other states paid it no attention whatever.

Until 1953. Then, suddenly, two things happened. The first was that in England, a Royal Commission on Capital Punishment recommended abrogating the long-established knowledge-of-right-and-wrong test and leaving "the jury to determine whether the accused was suffering from disease of the mind (or mental deficiency) to such a degree that he ought not to be held responsible"—a rule that would if anything go rather beyond the New Hampshire formula.

The second was that in this country, less than a year later, the Court of Appeals for the District of Columbia adopted the New Hampshire rule expressly. In *Durham* v. *United States*,[11] the court repudiated the old right-and-wrong test and the irresistible-impulse test which together had theretofore constituted the law in the District, and held:

The rule we now hold must be applied on the retrial of this case and in future cases is not unlike that followed by the New Hampshire court since 1870. It is simply that an accused is not criminally responsible if his unlawful act was the product of mental disease or mental defect. . . .

The legal and moral traditions of the western world re-

quire that those who, of their own free will and with evil
intent (sometimes called *mens rea*), commit acts which violate the law, shall be criminally responsible for those acts.
Our traditions also require that where such acts stem from
and are the product of a mental disease or defect as those
terms are used herein, moral blame shall not attach, and
hence there will not be criminal responsibility. The rule we
state in this opinion is designed to meet these requirements.[12]

The Durham decision touched off a flood of articles
and comments in the law reviews and medical-legal journals.[13] No other case in years has aroused as much comment in the professional journals. The psychiatrists have
almost unanimously hailed it as a great step forward,
and even the lawyers, conservative as they traditionally
are, have been at least cautiously respectful, although
they have raised a number of serious doubts and difficulties. For a viewpoint that had had only one judicial
champion, who was last heard from eighty-five years ago,
this is certainly remarkable, and perhaps significant.
After eighty-five years of dormancy, Dr. Ray's suggestion
that the rule "will finally be accepted everywhere" may
yet come true.

These recent developments make it appropriate to
consider the advantages and the difficulties presented in
this relatively new and untried rule which nevertheless
traces back to Dr. Ray's writings of more than a century
ago. Specifically, we shall compare this "product rule"
(as we may call it for want of a better label) with the
established right-and-wrong and irresistible-impulse

tests, and more particularly with another important new development, the Model Penal Code being drafted by the American Law Institute.

First, it is necessary to examine the existing law, and to ask whether it need be changed at all.

CHAPTER TWO

The M'Naghten Rule

The question that the legal "tests" of insanity are designed to answer is not: "What was the defendant's mental condition at the time of the act?" Rather, it is: "What should be done with him?"

It is worth emphasizing this, for too often critics, especially psychiatrists, seem to assume that the test is an attempt on the part of lawyers to define mental disorder by the enumeration of certain symptoms. The test makes *no* attempt to define mental disorder; what it defines are the *effects* that the disorder must produce if it is to absolve the defendant from criminal responsibility. It is a formula for answering the question, what to do with him.

What is involved specifically is the drawing of a line between the use of public agencies and public force to condemn the offender by conviction, with resultant sanctions in which there is inescapably a punitive ingredient (however constructive we may attempt to make the process of correction) and modes of disposition in which that ingredient is absent, even though restraint may be involved. To put the matter differently, the problem is to discriminate between the cases where a punitive-correctional disposition is approprate and those in which a medical-custodial disposition is the only kind that the law should allow.[1]

But law cannot operate in a vacuum. A sound rule for distinguishing the legally irresponsible from the responsible cannot ignore the current psychiatric knowledge of the relationship of mental disorder to antisocial behavior. A sound rule must permit medical evidence on every facet of the defendant's mental condition that will help determine his responsibility or irresponsibility. The established legal rule, however, does ignore current psychiatric knowledge, and is based on an obsolete and false conception of the nature of mental disorder.

"The established legal rule" is, of course, the so-called right-and-wrong test: was the accused so mentally disordered "as not to know the nature and quality of the act he was doing, or, if he did know it, that he did not know he was doing what was wrong?"

This wording comes from M'Naghten's case, an advisory opinion handed down by the judges of England in 1843.[2] There are few rules of law, in any field, that date back that far. There are still fewer instances, under our system of *stare decisis,* of a mere advisory opinion carrying *any* weight as a precedent. *This* advisory opinion has carried and still carries probably more weight than any actual decision in history, with the possible exception of Shelley's case. Shelley's case has been largely abrogated by statutes, but the Opinion in M'Naghten's case still provides our main test of criminal irresponsibility, and is the *sole* test in England and in twenty-nine of the American states.[3] This in spite of the fact that it deals with a science in which there have been revolutionary changes during the century and more that has intervened, and in spite of the fact that the opinion was not a particularly enlightened statement even for its own time. There is evidence that, in the words of Judge Biggs in last year's Isaac Ray lectures, "the Queen and the lords put a hot fire to the feet of the judges of England."[4] The period was one of unrest and there had been a number of attempts to assassinate English sovereigns and their ministers. The judges were in effect called to account for what seemed to be miscarriages of justice. Had circumstances been more favorable, they might have reshaped the law in accordance with enlightened views then already available. As it was, they presented a verbose set of answers to questions, which froze the law "in a mold which was divorced from reality,"[5] and which seems to represent a retreat from what had already been accepted as law in the trial of Hadfield, forty-three years before.[6]

Most psychiatrists consider the M'Naghten rule to be unsound. Their main complaint, to state it as briefly as possible, is that the test is fallacious in its assumption that incapacity to know the nature and quality of an act or incapacity to know its wrongfulness is the only significant symptom of mental disorder and the only integrator and guide of conduct, and consequently should be the only criterion of responsibility. It is fallacious in thus concentrating on cognition and ignoring other aspects of mentation—volition and emotion. In some states, the volitional aspect is taken into account under the so-called irresistible-impulse test. But that still largely ignores emotion.

The test also wholly ignores the role played by the unconscious. That is hardly strange because the test antedates Freud by half a century. It was Sigmund Freud's investigations that led to our understanding of the unconscious, that submerged part of our mind which so largely controls our basic attitudes and prejudices, guides our behavior, and deludes us about our motives. The criminal is even more likely than the rest of us to be jerked like an automaton by stormy, bitter emotions so deep-seated that he is not himself conscious of them. No lawyer, no judge, no one charged with the task of trying to learn why criminals behave as they do, should be ignorant of the role played by the unconscious in guiding human actions. But the law's test is officially so ignorant. And because Freudian psychology emphasizes that the unconscious is largely the realm of sexual and other primitive impulses, it encounters not only ignorance but actual antagonism from some judges who are offended by what they feel is an unnecessarily nasty realism.

The unconscious helps explain not only why criminals behave as they do, but also why the rest of us behave as we do toward criminals. Our righteous indignation against wrongdoers is more often than we consciously realize an expression of our own strong but repressed aggressive impulses. The urge to punish in others the misconduct we repress in ourselves is probably the main obstacle to the adoption of a rational penal code.

It is not hard to understand why the law should ignore the volitional, emotional and unconscious aspects of mentation and concentrate on capacity to know. Not only lawyers, but philosophers and laymen also tend to regard intellection as the core of mental conduct. We tend to define all other mental-conduct concepts in terms of cognition. We assume that the one important mental function is finding answers to questions, and that any other occupations of our minds are merely applications of such answers or even regrettable distractions from their consideration.

Psychology itself a hundred years ago was concerned largely with cognition. It is only in more recent years that we have come to appreciate the fundamental importance of the conative-affective aspects of mental activity, and the difficulty of maintaining neat separations between activities that shade into one another.

The M'Naghten rule's concentration on capacity to "know" as the only relevant aspect of mentation reflects, naturally enough, the scientific thinking that was current when the rule was formulated. It reflects the 19th century faculty psychology which assumed that "knowing" was one of several disparate mental faculties, each of which had its own locus in a particular part of the brain.[7]

Faculty psychology, in turn, reflected still older notions. When the word "psychology" was coined, two hundred years ago, the prevalent doctrine, stemming

mainly from Descartes, was that every (normal) human
being has both a body and a mind. Underlying this was
the still broader assumption that there are two kinds of
existence, physical and mental. What has physical existence is composed of Matter; what has mental existence
consists of Mind.[8] This method of description is often
traced to Aristotle. Actually, it goes back to the way of
thinking of very ancient man, who saw everything, including himself, as having a "spirit" inside, much as a
person lives in a room.[9]

The psyche versus soma dualism was pretty well ven-
tilated in the early 19th century, but it continues strong
today, and it certainly was not questioned by the judges
of England in 1843. Under the influence of this assumed
contrast between Mind and Matter, we tend to think of
ourselves as if we were a body occupied by a person[10]—
a Ghost in the Machine, as one English philosopher has
called it. We speak as if inside each of us there is a spirit
which we variously call Reason, Consciousness, or the
Soul. Sometimes we talk as if we are inhabited by a trin-
ity of such ghosts: Thought, Will and Emotion.[11]

But a lot has happened in psychiatry since that time.
It is hardly an exaggeration to say that everything in psychiatry has happened since that time. And modern
psychiatry does not conceive "that there is a separate
little man in the top of one's head called reason whose
function it is to guide another unruly little man called
instinct, emotion or impulse in the way he should go."[12]
To modern psychology, reason, emotion and impulse
are regarded not as disparate functions, but as wholly

interdependent and interacting manifestations of the
unitary personality. As Dr. Winfred Overholser said in
delivering the first Isaac Ray lectures in 1952:

What we generally term "mind" is an abstraction, an in-
clusive word which signifies the sum total of the ways in
which the individual acts as a whole in response to the stim-
uli, internal and external, which are constantly playing
upon him.[13]

In mental no less than in physical illness, when a person is ill, he is ill all over.

As a matter of fact, the most competent psychiatrists
had already begun to appreciate this when the M'Naghten rule was written. Isaac Ray had already written, at
least five years before M'Naghten's case, "The animal
economy is a whole; no part of it can exist without the
rest, nor be injured or abstracted without marring the
energy or harmony of the whole system."[14]

Not only are intellection, volition and emotion inex-
tricably interwoven, but it is probably emotion and not
intellection that is the most important of these. "Perhaps the outstanding feature of modern criminal psychiatry," said Sir Norwood East, "is the recognition of
the importance of the emotional rather than the intellectual genesis of crime."[15]

"It has become a commonplace among those who deal
with mental illness and behavior problems," said Sheldon and Eleanor Glueck in their study, *Unraveling
Juvenile Delinquency*, "that the emotional-volitional or
temperamental make-up of the human being is usually

more determinative of conduct and character than the intellectual."[16]

How we respond to any given stimulus or situation depends upon a complex of psychological processes, of which "reasoning" or "logical thinking" constitutes a fraction unflatteringly small for a creature who calls himself Homo sapiens. Passion can distort our judgment to such a degree as almost completely to destroy our ability to judge objectively.

These basic insights of modern psychology have been appreciated by the more perceptive leaders of the legal profession. In 1929, Mr. Justice Cardozo told us that the present legal definition "has little relation to the truths of mental life."[17] More recently, the Solicitor General of the United States, Simon E. Sobeloff, warned that "what we ought to fear above all is not the absence of a definition, but being saddled with a false definition. We must avoid the rigidity which precludes inquiry, which shuts out light and insists on concepts that are at odds with things known and acknowledged not only by the medical profession but by all informed men."[18]

But most lawyers and judges are still able to convince themselves that the right-and-wrong test remains sound because most of us still think of the "insane" in the way that was general in 1843. We still tend to think that such persons must be creatures wholly unlike ourselves, whose capacity to reason is either practically non-existent or whose modes of reasoning are fantastically different from our own.

This way of thinking stems from a time—only a little

over a century ago—when even physicians assumed that disease was a state wholly different from health. Especially was this true of mental disease, which was frequently attributed to demoniac possession or a visitation from God (apparently there was some disagreement in theological diagnosis). Virchow (1821-1902) was apparently the first to advance the view that the processes of disease are quite analogous to the normal processes of life, differing from them only in degree.

We would understand mental illness better if we thought of it as similar to physical illness. Few of us function so perfectly that we can't appreciate what illness means. And if we think a bit about our own mental processes, we ought to be able to appreciate what mental illness is. We all try to escape from unhappy thoughts and memories by repressing them. We remember the "good old days," and forget what was bad about them. Most of us have felt depressed at times. At other times, in the high spirits of youth or under the influence of more synthetic spirits, we have experienced something of the manic patient's euphoria. We all look for excuses for our failures; it is not hard for us to believe that we are being discriminated against or persecuted if we fail to gain the recognition we think we deserve. And when reality is too harsh, most of us seek some escape, in liquor, in escapist literature or in escapist religion. The psychotic patient has merely carried these common human traits farther than most of us. While most of us day-dream once in a while, the schizophrenic has retreated entirely into a dream world. Whereas most of us feel abused or picked on only occasionally, the paranoiac has convinced himself that there is a gigantic and fearful conspiracy against him. Most of us feel blue at times; the depressed patient finds life so intolerable that he is likely to commit suicide.[19]

In short, the mentally ill are like the rest of us, only more so. If lawyers could study actual cases of mental illness in the flesh, jointly with a psychiatrist, we would quickly see this. We'd see what is meant by "alteration of personality" and by the indivisible unity of personality.[20] Since we cannot here study actual patients, let me present at least a word picture of an actual case.

This is the story of Edward G., the college student mentioned at the beginning of Chapter I, who on a sudden impulse one day choked a young woman to death. It is not a case that illustrates any single clear-cut concept. If it is helpful, it is rather because it represents the really difficult cases, for which no solution is readily apparent.

The facts of the case have been fully recounted in a book by Richard Gehman, entitled *A Murder in Paradise*. The following account is a summary from Gehman's book.

Eddie was born in Pitman, New Jersey, in 1924. Dr. Edward A. Strecker, an eminent psychiatrist who examined him after his arrest for murder, stated that he was "very definitely spoiled by his parents and was inadequately prepared to meet the stresses of every-day life. . . . His mother . . . was definitely an emotionally possessive parent. . . . He never received adequate preparation and training for leading a reasonably satisfactory personal and social adult life."

Gehman in his book calls this a "cautious understatement." Mrs. G. was "high-strung" and had had a "nervous breakdown." "Her husband has been described by acquaintances as a mild-mannered, inoffensive, almost ineffectual man, who must have been unaware of, or unable to do anything about, his wife's extremely protective attitude toward their son. A neighbor remembers that when little Eddie, as he was always called, was put out to play in the yard behind the house, Mrs. G. either poked her head out the door or ran outside every five or ten minutes to have a look at him."

Whenever Eddie went out with another boy for a hike or to play ball, his mother told him to be careful and not to get hurt, and would repeat the warning over and over.

The mother's disposition affixed itself to the boy. One of his elementary school teachers, who had taught for twenty years, recalled him as one of the most nervous children ever to sit in her room. Although he had an I.Q. of 119-120, he graduated seventy-eighth in a high school class of seventy-eight.

He was an athletic star in high school and was, as he himself said, "a big frog in a little pond." "Perhaps," as Gehman suggests, "because he was secretly a physical coward and needed to prove himself, perhaps because he was seeking from the outside world the attention and applause and approval he received so copiously at home, whatever the reason he excelled in sports as few students have in the entire history of Pitman High."

His father and mother were his most avid fans. They attended every game, even those with schools miles away from home. And they cheered him vociferously from the stands.

It was in sports events that Eddie first began to exhibit the quick temper that friends later called his outstanding characteristic. He was a poor loser. Once, after his team had lost a close game, friends found him in the dressing room in an uncontrollable rage beating his fists against the metal lockers.

He was a flashy dresser and while he was apparently not actually very popular with the girls, he liked to give the impression that he was. Dr. Strecker later said:

"The pattern of his sex life was, in my opinion, definitely abnormal. In his boyhood he never masturbated. I quite believe the statement since [he] is sufficiently well informed to know that there is nothing unusual or abnormal in a certain amount of masturbation in boyhood, and in fact it occurs in an overwhelmingly large percentage of boys at some stage of their development. During his high school years, and before, [he] had no sex relationships of any kind. In fact he had no sex relationships until he was overseas with the Army in Italy."

After graduating from high school in 1943 he enlisted in the Army Air Force for pilot training. After about six months he failed his tests and was declared ineligible to continue pilot training. Instead he worked as a control tower operator.

Eddie was left-handed. His parents made him learn to write with his right hand and tried to get him to eat with it, but he remained left-handed in most other things, including throwing a baseball or a football. After two years in the Air Force, he was mustered out. His parents insisted that he go to college and he entered Franklin and Marshall. His record was poor. He was placed on probation once and threatened with it at least twice more. Some of his friends felt that his feeling of inadequacy in college stemmed from his inability to star in athletics. He went out for football and for basketball, but failed to make either team. While still in school he married a girl from his home town. They had financial troubles and mother-in-law troubles. The sexual aspect of the marriage was not satisfactory. They did not want a baby, but the wife objected to the use of any contraceptives, and so withdrawal was practiced. "The whole pattern of his sex life," said Dr. Strecker, "is one of immaturity and inadequacy."

After the first year of married life his friends noticed that he was developing a habit of affectionate conduct toward other girls — in what was supposed to be a joking kind of way. He was quick to kiss them on the cheek, put his arm around them, make remarks that were a bit *risqué* or make jocular proposals like, "Let's go out to the park and neck." This was all done in a joking way, but some of the girls thought he was not joking at all.

By the senior year in school the marriage began to

disintegrate. There were payments due on a car Eddie
had bought, payments due to a finance company, school
and fraternity bills. His wife was working, but her pay
check was less than $45 a week. She wanted to have a
child, in the hope that it might bolster up their marriage, but he was adamant; he was frantic to quit school
and make money instead of pinching pennies at college.

Apparently his wife began to worry about his personality because she induced him to go to the Guidance
Center at the college and take some tests. The couple
went home to Pitman for the 1949 Christmas holidays,
staying part of the time in the home of each of their
parents. He went through a depressing emotional experience when he told his mother that he might not gradu-
ate because of poor grades. She got very excited and
started to cry. When he returned to the campus he was
in a terrible emotional state. Gehman states the situation
with perception:

"The worries, fears, guilts and doubts inside him
could be contained no longer. They had to be released;
he had to do something—to release them, to prove to
himself that he was a man, and to prove it to the world.
He could not have been consciously aware of his need;
he could never have articulated it in detail. If it had
been suggested to him, he probably would have scoffed.
Intimations of inner violence are intolerable to one so
bent upon being socially acceptable. They exist only in
others; in less respectable people, not in fraternity
brothers or athletes or campus politicians. Yet the pow-
erfully assertive impulses were there, and the conscious

of Edward G. shut itself off, for a time, and obeyed its
lower, darker brother. On Tuesday, January 10, 1950,
he met Marian Louise Baker, took her for a ride, and
killed her."

He was never able to say later exactly why he killed
the girl. He had gone downtown with the idea of seeing
a movie. He happened to meet the girl on the street. He
knew who she was, but had never been a close friend.
She accepted his invitation to take a ride in his car, and
they drove out past the country club. There, according
to his written statement to the police, "I stopped the car,
reached over and choked her. She screamed and got out
of the car and I chased her. She didn't get very far. I
continued choking her. Then I went and got the keys
out of the car and opened it up and got the lug wrench.
I hit her with it, I don't know how many times. I pulled
her body down below the knoll by the garbage pile,
threw her pocket book away, not too far, and got back
in my car and drove back to the college. . . ."

He was aware of the pressures and other resentments
stirring inside him but only vaguely. His own explanation was that "I did it on an impulse." He did not, perhaps he could not, say more. The word "impulse"
apparently seemed to him to be explanation enough.
But this was almost certainly not what the law would
recognize as an irresistible impulse, even where that is a
defense, which it is not in Pennsylvania.

Gehman offers a fuller explanation when he says that
in battering the girl's head to an almost unrecognizable
mass, ". . . he was not merely killing her. All his life,

women had loomed over him as vicious symbols of authority, tantalizing, shadowy mistresses who controlled him and yet who taunted him by remaining ever out of grasp. While they used him as they wished, they whispered that he could dominate them—but he could not. They were too tricky, too elusive, too ultimately unattainable. Every mundane problem confronting him on the afternoon of January tenth was in some way connected with a woman. He could not bear it. The hostility, festering perhaps from the time he had been trained to the toilet, screamed for release. He did not simply kill Marian Baker. He killed his mother, teachers in school who had twisted him into learning, nurses in the Army hospital, whores in Italy, laughing and witless Pitman girls, his wife, his wife's friends, his friends' wives and girls, girls he saw on Lancaster and Pitman streets, girls he observed while at work in his various part-time jobs, every girl and every woman he had hated and simultaneously wanted. He murdered them all."

Dr. Strecker gave it as his opinion that the defendant was "extremely immature, very insecure, and very inadequate in his personality." Later in his testimony he said:

> . . . while I do not believe Eddie . . . was totally irresponsible, or completely incapable of distinguishing between right and wrong, yet I believe very strongly and very definitely his degree of responsibility, both medical and legal, must be assessed at very much less than that of the normal person, and that in both the psychiatric and legal sense he has an abnormal personality, and at the time of the crime and at this time has a latent psychosis, or mental disease,

schizophrenia. . . . Therefore I [say] his responsibility must be assessed at much less than the average person. . . . I therefore believe he did not have sufficient or average capacity to understand the nature and quality of his act.

The jury, after deliberating for four and a half hours, found the defendant guilty of murder in the first degree, and fixed the penalty at death. He died in the electric chair on April 23, 1951.

The facts of this case have been related at length because only from illustrative cases can we get a sense of how mental abnormality actually manifests itself. The case is not intended to prove any contention. It cannot be shown that executing this young man was a miscarriage of justice. This was not a case of gross and obvious disorder. But that is exactly why it is the hard kind of case. The raving maniacs and the drooling idiots are easy to spot, and juries are not likely to have difficulty in assessing their condition. The hard cases are those that are more or less like this one.

Revising the test would not make these hard cases easy, nor would it necessarily have produced a different result in Eddie's case. But a more realistic rule would at least have permitted a more realistic appraisal of his actual condition, instead of focusing on whether he knew right from wrong. Of course he knew that killing was wrong, and if that is the test, the problem is easy; he was responsible and properly punishable. The trouble is that this makes it too easy, for even the most seriously disordered psychotics usually know that much. As Dr. Philip Q. Roche of Philadelphia has said, any intelligent parent and anyone else who has had experience in child rearing knows that behavior problems are not merely a matter of failure to "know" what is wrong. When we are concerned about a child's bed wetting, thumb sucking, or temper tantrums, or cruel conduct toward pets or other children, we are likely nowadays to consult a doctor, but we don't demand that the doctor confine his examination to the question of whether the child "knows" better.[21]

Criminal law "is our child rearing system for grown-ups."[22] But it is preoccupied with whether the wrong-doer "knew better." It ignores emotional drives, unconscious motivations and all the other factors that not only every psychiatrist, but every intelligent mother knows are also highly relevant.

"Why is it that delinquents so earnestly promise and so often actually intend, to be good, yet so frequently fail to live up to their promises and intentions? The answer is that deeply-anchored, subsurface, and frequently unconscious forces are too powerful to be modified by a kindly talk with a judge or probation officer, or by the threat of punishment. Admonishing the child, exacting promises of good behavior, threatening with commitment, fining parents—all these are relatively superficial means of dealing with the problem."[23]

Failure to appreciate the role of the unconscious makes us fail to understand the true nature of many crimes. In sex offenses, for example, the obvious motive, sexual gratification, is not always the real one. Studies of sex offenders show that there is an unconscious motivation at work in many cases which is quite different. Bernard Glueck reports that 68 percent of the sex offenders examined by him in Sing Sing denied that they had any or more than partial sexual gratification at the time of their offense. "The most common motivation," he reported, "is the attempt to prove that they are sexually potent, that they are not castrated, and that their sexual function is normal. This need arises from the very intense feelings of genital inadequacy and impotence suffered by these men."[24]

There is also likely to be an unconscious motivation at work on those who punish the sex offender. Ironically, while the sexual impulse is often less strong in the sex offender than we suppose, it is often much stronger in the rest of us. The urge to punish sex offenders is strong because we know how strong the sexual impulse is in ourselves; consciously or unconsciously we fear that we might do what the sex offender has done. This disturbing thought we exorcise by publicly repudiating the wicked wretch and piously calling for his punishment.

Among the most curious manifestations of the unconscious is the wish to be punished. There are individuals who, tortured by the memory of some secret wrongdoing—or even some wholly imaginary wrongdoing—are so overwhelmed by a sense of guilt that they actually seek punishment. Often this seeking is below the level of consciousness, but it is there. The exhibitionist who repeats his act day after day at the same place and time, the "accident prone," the killer who leaves some strangely careless clue, or who feels called upon to do something to attract suspicion to himself afterward—all these are likely to be driven by some deep-seated guilt feelings to conduct that will lead to punishment.

This notion of a desire for punishment will strike the layman when he first encounters it as bizarre and far-fetched—one of those rather imaginative psychoanalytic concepts that laymen sometimes find so hilariously funny. But if one reads the life histories of some of these persons, and comes to appreciate how intense these guilt feelings are, one can see why psychiatrists accept the phenomenon as very real.

Overwhelming and insufferable guilt feelings in fact occur much more frequently than incapacity to know the wrongfulness of a criminal act. It is the M'Naghten notion that is farfetched.

As Dr. Gregory Zilboorg said years ago, ". . . except for totally deteriorated, drooling, hopeless psychotics of long standing, and congenital idiots—who seldom commit murder or have the opportunity to commit murder—the great majority and perhaps all murderers know what they are doing, the nature and quality of their act, and the consequences thereof, and they are therefore 'legally sane' regardless of the opinion of any psychiatrist."[25]

But overawareness of the wrongfulness of one's acts is all too common. In the depressive phase of manic-depressive psychosis the patient is likely to feel that he has committed unforgivable sins, that he is worthless, a

burden to his family, a damned soul. Suppose a person
in such a depression decides to commit suicide, and to
take his family with him, to save them also from the
sufferings of the world. This is no mere imaginary situation; it is exactly what is likely to happen in such cases.
Every depressed patient is a serious suicide risk. The
right and wrong test would make such persons criminally responsible, yet probably most of us would feel
that responsibility should not justly be imposed in such
cases.

It is ironic but true that "good" people experience
more guilt feelings than "bad" people. A good person is
one who exercises a lot of self-control in shunning temp-
tation. Such a person necessarily does a good deal more
thinking about these temptations than the person who
yields easily. The good girl feels a good deal more
ashamed about an illicit kiss or even her own sinful
thoughts than the bad girl about her misdeeds. We call
the latter a woman of easy virtue; it's a good term, and
with reverse English we may call the former a woman of
uneasy virtue. Guilt feelings and an uneasy virtue are
the price the good person pays for not being bad. Sometimes the price is higher—loss of one's sanity. Faced with
inner conflicts that they cannot resolve except in either
acting out in crime or living out in mental illness, people have gone mad to avoid crime. Instead of committing actual crime, they begin to manifest conduct that
their relatives and friends can only call crazy, but which
is actually a symbolical and allegorical acting out of
their criminal impulses.[26] Of what use is a test of knowl-

edge of right and wrong to these poor wretches, whose failing is an all too painfully strong knowledge of right and wrong?

The law's conception of how the human personality functions is as defective as was the 1843 conception of the structure of the atom. As much progress has been made in the last century in psychology and psychiatry as in physics. It is as frustrating to try to force modern psychiatric diagnoses into the discarded concepts and terms of a hundred years ago, as to force scientists to describe nuclear physics in terms of matter made up of atoms and molecules only.

Suppose if we asked a physicist on the witness stand to explain nuclear fission and he started talking of the composition of the nucleus in terms of protons, neutrons and mesons, we were to stop him and say that the law is not interested in these concepts, but recognizes only atoms and molecules and that therefore he must make his explanation in those terms only. That is not an unfair comparison with what we ask of the psychiatric expert. He is trying to explain the behavior of an atom of humanity, one personality. That personality is, in modern psychiatric conception, a highly complex organization, whose behavior is governed by the interaction of its various components and its environment.

Today intelligent laymen, including some lawyers, are beginning to understand the psychiatrists' view of human personality and of human behavior, and to want to bring the law into accord with it.

CHAPTER THREE

The Search for Certainty

Perhaps the primary objection that has been raised against Dr. Ray's product rule is that it would submit the insanity defense to the jury without giving them the guidance of any definite formula or criterion.

"The advantage of a formula," it is said, "is that it serves to limit the arbitrary element and to promote uniformity as well as to help the jury to decide between conflicting views. It is as much a safeguard for the offender in some cases as in others it is a safeguard against unjustifiable acquittals on the ground of insanity. To have no rule at all would be to leave the decision on which often a man's life depends to the uncertain variations of ethical standard and emotional reaction which may influence the minds of members of a jury."[1]

Since the decision as to responsibility must be made by laymen, to whom the expert witnesses in their testimony and the judge in his instructions must communicate, it is a desideratum if not an essential of any rule that it lend itself to communication with the jury. A rule that jurors can understand and apply with some ease not only helps them decide a difficult question, but also helps obtain uniformity of decisions by different juries, and so helps attain our ideal of "equal justice under law." To the extent that a clear rule could eliminate arbitrariness of decision it would also relieve the juror of personal moral responsibility for the decision. The juryman's task is onerous enough at best. In a serious case it is distressing to have to find a man guilty even when the juror is shielded from guilt feelings by the knowledge that the law is clear and permits no other verdict. If the law is unclear and leaves the decision to the conscience of the jury with no definite rule to bind him, the burden can be more than we have a right to impose.

A definite rule would also aid predictability of results. Where the prosecutor could predict that the defendant would be acquitted on the ground of insanity if brought to trial, he might be willing to allow him to be committed as incompetent to stand trial, or accept a plea of not guilty by reason of insanity. Conversely, an unpredictable rule may encourage merely frivolous and dilatory pleas of insanity.

A clear and definite rule may aid the defense in some cases. When a shocking crime has aroused public excitement and alarm, and the diagnosis is one of incurable and dangerous disorder, the jury's conscious or unconscious fear may lead it to vote for the death penalty as a kind of euthanasia. This may happen under any test, of course, but it would seem more likely to happen where the test is vague than where it is clear and the defendant clearly comes within it.

No, there is no doubt that a clear and simple rule would be a Good Thing. Clarity and simplicity are always desirable, and in law, they are rare and precious jewels among the heaps of scoriaceous dross produced by the legal mind at work.

Those who argue that the Durham case rule is too indefinite say or at least assume that the existing law is less so. The main argument for the traditional right-and-wrong test has been that it satisfies the need for a rule that is clear and certain. Its adherents admit that it is old. Most of them today are ready to concede that it is based on an outmoded and fallacious psychological premise, which concentrates on *intellection* as the only relevant aspect of mental responsibility, and ignores volition, emotion and the influence of the unconscious. They concede that in ignoring the factor of volition, it is even *legally* unsound, since capacity to choose whether to do or refrain from doing the act is regarded as essential under any civilized concept of criminal intent and responsibility. Judges and writers have sometimes admitted that the test ought logically to be broadened, but have refused to broaden it because they feared the broader test would be too uncertain, too difficult to prove or disprove, or to easy and therefore too dangerous.[2] In short, we are told that it is necessary to sacrifice both scientific validity and legal logic in the interest of certainty.

Unfortunately, when we try to lay down a pat and simple rule to cover complex and varying situations, we wind up with either (1) a rule that is too rigid and which we find we have to circumvent by fictions, by spurious interpretations, by administrative dodges or by open or covert violation; or (2) a rule that is so general and indefinite that it actually says nothing—like "a person is not negligent if he exercises due care."

Let us look at the right-and-wrong test and see whether it is as clear and simple as sometimes assumed. At first reading, it does seem commendably clear. Compared to the recondite polysyllables that laymen associate with legal language, or the equally esoteric jargon of psychiatry, this is practically basic English. But is it clear and easily understood? Let us take a sharper look at some of these simple words, and ask what they mean. What is meant by knowing the "nature and quality" of the act? "A madman who believes that he is squeezing lemons when he chokes his wife," to quote an example from the comments to the Model Penal Code being drafted by the American Law Institute, would obviously not know the nature and quality of his act. (I put aside the possibility that he's right; that she *is* a lemon.) But suppose he *knows* it is his wife, but chokes her because of a delusion that God had commanded him to do so, for the salvation of mankind. He would know the *physical* nature of his act, but would he know its quality? Does the word quality refer to a different aspect of perception from "nature," or do the two words mean the same thing? After 112 years we still don't know. In an English case decided in 1916, it was held that the two words mean only one thing—and that that one meaning is limited to knowledge of the physical nature of the act.[3] That seems to leave the words "and quality" as mere surplusage. Is this English interpretation law in this country? There is no discussion of this question in the cases. And certainly the words themselves don't tell us. How clear is the test?

Not only is it not clear whether "nature" means something different from "quality"; there is not even agreement as to whether that whole phrase, "nature and quality," means anything different from knowledge that the act is "wrong." Some cases omit reference to "nature and quality" entirely and word the test simply in terms of whether the defendant knew that the act was "wrong." Suppose a Pennsylvania trial judge worded the test that way in his instructions to the jury. Would that be material error? There are no Pennsylvania cases on it. New York has held that this would be error. Two or three other states have said no, it would make no difference. Still other courts seem to *assume* that it makes no difference, because they use both forms of wording and apparently regard them as synonymous.[4] How clear is the wording?

If both parts of the test are used, does it matter whether they are joined conjunctively or disjunctively? The Pennsylvania court had that question before it as recently as 1953, in the Smith case.[5]

And what about the word "know," the key word in the knowledge test? As just said, a man may know the physical nature of the act, but he may be quite incapable of comprehending its true significance. The man charged with choking his wife may have known it was his wife's throat he was squeezing, but his understanding of the act and its wrongfulness may be on a superficial, verbal level, without any real insight into its full significance or its consequences for her or for himself. That is, his knowledge of its wrongfulness may be only like that of a small child who knows it is "naughty" to hit his baby sister with a hammer, but who can't distinguish the naughtiness of breaking the head of a doll from that of bashing in sister's skull.[6]

It has been argued that "knowing" denotes not only insight into the significance of the act, but also ability to make use of such knowledge.[7] Most courts would probably reject such broad interpretation of the word "know." But if such an interpretation were ably presented by counsel, is it certain that a given court would not accept it? Does the wording of the rule clearly exclude it?

The concept of "wrong" is patently ambiguous. Does it mean morally wrong, or illegal? Does the man who knew the act was against the law, but who heard God command him to do it, know that the act was "wrong"? A few cases have held one way—and a few have held the other.[8] How clear is the test?

I could go on. Let it suffice, however, to add only a quotation from Professor Sheldon Glueck. Thirty years ago, in his authoritative book, *Mental Disorder and the Criminal Law,* he said:

Perhaps in no other field of American law is there so much disagreement as to fundamentals and so many contradictory decisions in the same jurisdictions. Not a modern text or compilation begins the discussion of the subject of insanity and its relation to the criminal law without a doleful reference to the chaos in this field.[9]

So much for the notion that the right-and-wrong test has given us clarity and certainty in the law.

The ambiguities mentioned above are all within the law itself. That is, they are ambiguities concerning the meaning of strictly legal concepts. We get into other ambiguities when we try to translate these legal concepts into psychiatric ones, or vice versa, because the fact is that this traditional right-and-wrong test does not fit into present-day psychiatric thinking, and it cannot be made to fit. The law simply does not talk the same language as the psychiatrist.

In consequence, it is almost impossible for the psychiatrist in a court room to say anything that seems to him meaningful. We do earnestly seek the psychiatrist's opinion on the defendant's condition, but we insist that he talk our language. Oh, we may let the witness talk a while in his own way, but ultimately we insist that he get down to *the* issue—did the defendant at the time of the act know the nature and quality of the act, and if so, did he know that it was wrong? That is the "clear and easy" test of which we are so proud. But the psychiatrist doesn't find it easy. He doesn't find it at all easy.

Suppose it is his opinion that the accused knew the *physical* nature of his act, but had no real appreciation of its enormity, its significance or its implications; also that the accused if asked, and if he gave a truthful answer, would be able to say he knew it was wrong. But he is seriously psychotic; his disorder has significantly affected his personality, his outlook and his behavior; and the psychiatrist is convinced that the act can be attributed to the disorder. How is he to testify? On the witness stand he is not asked merely to explain his diagnosis, his conclusions and his reasons therefor; he must address himself to a concept that has no validity in his eyes. To make sense of the lawyers' questions he must translate the legalistic concepts they insist he talk about into the psychiatric realities that he knows about.

There are no scientific formulae or guides for this job of translation.[10] Each witness must make his own subjective interpretations. In practice, he will probably resolve the difficulty by equating the aspects of deviation that the law considers relevant with deviation from the normal generally. In other words, he will be inclined to act on the assumption that if the person is seriously disordered, his capacity to understand or to conform is equally disordered. It is no secret that many psychiatrists do that right now; if the person is suffering from a psychosis, they find him "insane" within the legal test, otherwise not. Others probably work out other interpretations. To a large extent the witness must do his interpreting extemporaneously, in response to questions put to him on the stand. Not surprisingly, the experts retained by the prosecution tend to interpret the test so as to reach one conclusion, those retained by the defense, another. Yet both may in fact agree completely in their

clinical diagnoses; if allowed, they would probably have
no difficulty in agreeing on a joint report.

The frustrating blind alleys that we get into when we
insist on the medical witness' expressing a diagnosis in
terms of knowledge of right and wrong, is well illus-
trated in the Durham case itself. The only expert heard
in that case was asked whether he would say that
Durham knew the difference between right and wrong
on the date of the criminal act. He replied, "As I have
stated before, if the question of the right and wrong
were propounded to him he could give you the right
answer." Here the court interrupted and the following
colloquy took place:

The Court. "No, I don't think that is the question, Doctor
—not whether he could give a right answer to a question,
but whether he, himself, knew the difference between right
and wrong in connection with governing his own actions.
. . . If you are unable to answer, why, you can say so; I mean,
if you are unable to form an opinion."
The Witness. "I can only answer this way: That I can't tell
how much the abnormal thinking and the abnormal experiences in the form of hallucinations and delusions—delusions of persecution—had to do with his anti-social behavior.

"I don't know how anyone can answer that question
categorically, except as one's experience leads him to know
that most mental cases can give you a categorical answer of
right and wrong. But what influence these symptoms have
on abnormal behavior or anti-social behavior—"
The Court. "Well, your answer is that you are unable to
form an opinion, is that it?"
The Witness. "I would say that that is essentially true, for
the reasons that I have given."

Later, when defense counsel sought elaboration from the doctor on his answers relating to the "right and wrong" test, the court cut off the questioning, saying "you have answered the question, Doctor."[11]

As this colloquy shows, even when the psychiatrist tries to answer the question that the law regards as all-important, he is expected to do so categorically; his interpretations and explanations are likely to be brushed aside as irrelevant. In the Durham case, the doctor's effort to explain the difference between "knowledge" of wrongfulness on the merely verbal level and a more penetrating comprehension of the implications of the act was obviously of no interest to the trial judge. Did the accused know right from wrong—yes or no? That's the question, and the answer to that one question is all that really counts.

The psychiatrist knows that this is the crucial question. He knows that it doesn't ask merely for a medical opinion. In effect it asks the doctor to express his judgment as to whether the accused should be held guilty or not. He knows that if he says yes, the defendant knew that the act was wrong, he is saying that he is legally sane and punishable, although his own opinion actually may be that the accused is seriously disordered and that the act was committed in consequence of the disorder. Should he say no? That answer would perhaps come closer to expressing his true judgment that the defendant was not mentally responsible for his act, but, strictly and literally, it would be untrue. As the Group for the Advancement of Psychiatry has said, "This leaves the witness with his intellectual honesty at stake and no escape."[12] However he answers, cross-examination will reveal that he cannot give any relevant information about the defendant's condition without contradicting himself.

No wonder that so many of our ablest psychiatrists refuse to serve as expert witnesses. Their dissatisfaction with the traditional legal test has been well stated by Dr. Robert Waelder:

Many psychiatrists seem to resent a situation in which they are compelled to speak a language not their own, which they either feel to be prescientific or which they, rightly or wrongly, suspect to be loaded with metaphysical implications not easily perceived.

Clinical psychiatrists are used to thinking in terms of syndromes (such as delusions, hallucinations, depressions, elations, etc.) or of disease entities (such as schizophrenia, manic-depressive psychosis, etc.). Those who have absorbed psychoanalytic concepts are also accustomed to think in dynamic and genetic terms such as inner conflicts and their attempted solutions, and the conditioning by childhood experience. But in neither case do the terms "right" or "wrong," essential in applying the M'Naghten rule, or the concept of "knowing" the difference between right and wrong, carry a precise psychological or psychiatric meaning. . . . As a result, the psychiatrist is prevented from using the language in which he has been trained to organize his thoughts and in whch the meaning, the fringes of meaning and the implications of each term are familiar to him. Instead, he is forced to testify in a language not his own, and he cannot be sure of the implications which his words may seem to carry to the judge or to the jury.

Jurists sometimes do not seem to realize that this is a real problem. Since the words of the M'Naghten rule do not seem problematic to them, they are inclined to conclude that the reluctant psychiatrists are slow in fulfilling their civic duties or are actually trying to obstruct the administration of the law because they disapprove of it.[13]

We lawyers also expect the psychiatrist to give us *exact* answers. Psychiatry is Science, and like everyone in our twentieth century civilization, we have tremendous faith in what the scientific method can do. We don't distinguish very carefully between the medical and the physical sciences. We are sure that the physical sciences are marvelously exact, and we assume that medicine today is equally exact. In the trial of Eddie G., discussed in Chapter II, the prosecuting attorney cross-examining an expert witness for the defense, put this question to him:

Now, Doctor, I show you a ruler. Now, let us assume that the bottom of this ruler as it touches the witness stand here has reached the level of what we call legal insanity. Let's assume the top of the ruler . . . is a normal person. Where do you place [the defendant]?

The doctor, although saying that it was "just a guess," felt called upon to make such a guess, and he placed the defendant at 6¼ inches.[14]

We *expect* scientists to have testing devices by which they can give us such measurements. But they don't. The fact is, as Ranyard West has reminded us, that medicine, and especially psychiatry, is not yet an exact science. It is rather a mixture of science and art. Every one of the psychiatrist's most "confident statements about emotion, reason, and will tails off into uncertainty and inexactitude in matters of degree, completeness, or category."[15] Indeed, in the past hundred years, the manifestations of mental disorder have become more diffuse and less articulated in outspoken symptoms.[16]

Pending the millenium when psychiatrists will know all things, the lawyers will have to bear with such uncertainty and inexactitude, and to accept the fact that at best, the diagnosis of mental illness cannot be expressed wholly in terms of specific components but depends very largely upon clinical skill and experience which cannot wholly be verbalized.[17]

But I am not here to weep over the tribulations of psychiatrists who venture to take the witness stand as expert witnesses. What concerns us more is how all this effectuates what we said is the primary function of the test, to guide the jury. When the legal test is so meaningless to psychiatrists that the expert for the prosecution can come up with one conclusion and the expert for the defense with the contrary conclusion—although both may agree in their psychiatric diagnosis—have we really a test that provides a clear and simple guide for the jury? What too often happens is that the jury, noting only that the experts disagree in their conclusions as to whether the defendant was or was not "insane," are confused and irked by the apparent inexactitude of the science of psychiatry and the apparent venality of psychiatrists. So they throw out all the expert testimony and apply what they are pleased to call their common sense in deciding whether the fellow was crazy or not. When we are told that the product rule fails to give the jury a clear and easy yardstick to apply, I say we should look to how the right-and-wrong yardstick really works. For one thing, it should be interesting to learn how juries use the right-and-wrong test, to see if they find it as clear and simple as it is said to be. But the legal profession has traditionally preferred not to find out what actually goes on in the jury room. Now, however, a study of the jury process is being made at the University of Chicago Law School.

No findings have been published as yet, but the people in charge of the study have been good enough to give me their working papers on one specific study they have been running. That is an experiment in which the facts of the Durham case were presented to a number of mock juries. The jurors were drawn from the regular Chicago Municipal Court Jury Pool. They heard the evidence in the cases and deliberated and returned a verdict just as in an actual case. They were also asked to fill out questionnaires before the trial, after the trial but before deliberation, and after the jury verdict. Various factors were found to affect the juror's tendency to find the defendant sane and guilty, or insane: the juror's socio-economic status, his occupation, his education, whether he is white or Negro, even whether he is an Episcopalian or a Methodist, the seriousness of the crime charged, and the juror's general attitude toward criminals and punishment generally. But one factor that did *not* seem to affect the results was the instruc-

tions of the judge on the law governing insanity as a
defense. Half the juries were given the right-and-wrong
test in their instructions; the other half were given the
product rule. This did not seem to affect the verdicts
one way or the other. After the trial, the jurors were
told that there was another possible rule and were
asked (1) whether instructions giving the other rule
would have led the juror to a different decision; and (2)
which of the two rules the juror felt the court should
use in the future. There was little pattern to the results.
Some jurors who found the defendant insane under the
right-and-wrong test said they would have found him
sane under the product rule. Of those who found him
insane under the product rule, only one said he would
have found him sane under the right-and-wrong test.

These results accord with the actual facts of the
Durham case. In the first trial, where the jury was given
the right-and-wrong and irresistible impulse test, the
jury found Durham guilty. After reversal by the Court
of Appeals and the establishment of the new product
rule, Durham was retried. This jury, instructed under
the new rule, also found him guilty.[18]

The results also support what experienced judges and
lawyers have long told us—that juries decide the defense
of not guilty by reason of insanity on more pragmatic
bases than the written instructions.

Sir James Stephen told us that in 1883. "Juries," he
said, "care very little for generalities. In my experience
they are usually reluctant to convict if they look upon
the act itself as upon the whole a mad one, and to

acquit if they think it was an ordinary crime."[19] Seventy years later, the Lord Justice General of Scotland told the Royal Commission on Capital Punishment essentially the same thing. "However much you charge a jury as to the M'Naghten Rules or any other test," he said, "the question they would put to themselves when they retire is—'Is this man mad or is he not?'" The Commission felt that "English juries often do the same."[20] Experienced judges would say the same of American juries.[21]

"The most convincing answer," said the Royal Commission, to the argument that abolishing the rules would leave too large a task for the jury, "seems to us to be that they so often perform it already in cases where the application of the M'Naghten Rules would lead to a clearly wrong verdict."[22] No matter how the jury is charged, the way they actually approach the question in the jury room is probably pretty much in accord with the New Hampshire rule. They may not articulate it precisely, but if they are convinced that the defendant really was seriously disordered, and that it was this fact that led to the crime, they will usually acquit.

The way people function is probably determined as much by their personality dimensions and systems of values as by their methodology or the rules they profess to follow.[23] This is as true of jurors as of the rest of us. A juror functions as he does not merely because of the technical instructions given him by the judge, but also because of the system of values that he brings to the task. By system of values I include the contributions made by one's education, not only in school but in all

the experiences of one's life that have stimulated and
enriched, modified and chastened, one's capacity to
understand one's fellow human beings. The system of
values of the average man today is different from what it
was even a century ago. There has been a tremendous
spread of democracy and of regard for individual liberty
and for human dignity. We have more feeling for our
fellow human beings, including criminals. More and
more sincerely we are able to say: "There but for the
grace of God—or but for the grace of a strong super-ego
—go I." This is reflected in verdicts, even though the
law on the books may remain unchanged.

Not only psychiatrists and jurors, but lawyers and
judges too are confused by the ambiguities of the existing test. The test is not only a supposed guide to the
jury and an ultimate issue in the evidence; it is also a
method by which the appellate court controls the trial
judge. If the trial judge failed in his instructions to the
jury to state the test properly, the conviction may be
reversed. Whether the fatal verbal slip actually made
any difference is not asked. As I said, we do not try to
find out what actually happened in the jury room. It is
enough if the appellate court thinks that the error in
wording *might* have misled the jury. The result has
been described by a New York judge: ". . . as learned a
charge as the judges try to make, each interpreting the
statute in his own way, each being fortified by precedent,
each trying to lay down the correct legal test of responsibility, it is a poor lawyer who cannot find some flaw
in it upon which to argue for reversal. More cases in

which insanity is an issue are reversed for erroneous wording of the 'test,' or for refusal to grant correct instructions, or the giving of erroneous instructions regarding the test of insanity than for any other reason."[24]

That is in New York, where if anywhere the rule is clear, for there it is set down by statute. And the statute is very short and very simple. It says that the test is "such a defect of reason as (1) not to know the nature and quality of the act he was doing, or (2) not to know that the act was wrong." That's certainly commendably simple, if simplicity is our only goal. It's practically all in one- or two-syllable words. But even in New York, and certainly wherever else the right-and-wrong test is used, cases continue to arise on alleged errors in wording the test.

As I have already indicated, practically every word in the test has been the subject of judicial interpretation.

Even on so fundamental an issue as whether irresistible impulse is a defense or not, the law is not always clear even within a given jurisdiction. In Pennsylvania, for example, the cases from 1846 to at least 1925 had seemed to accept this as a defense. But during the last thirty years, the court, as I read its decisions, has seemed to repudiate it. Professor Louis Schwartz in 1951, however, told the Royal Commission that irresistible impulse is a defense. He seems to regard the repudiations as mere dicta.[25] In this state, therefore, the argument that it is necessary to have a single, clear test can be answered by pointing out that you have got along without clarity for a long time. The same uncertainty has existed in other states.[26]

Even where the irresistible impulse test has been specifically rejected, text writers and lawyers have sometimes argued that properly construed, the right-and-wrong test is broad enough to cover cases where volition is wholly or largely absent.[27] And in England, judges frequently do so interpret the M'Naghten rule. What sort of yardstick is this, whose markings mean nothing at all to psychiatrists, and mean one thing to some judges and something else to others?

American judges sometimes find some moral support in the thought that the M'Naghten rule remains the law of England. But while this is formally true, the law in action has changed very much in England since 1843. The *practice,* as distinguished from the rule-in-the-books, is already very close to what the product rule would provide. The severity of the M'Naghten rule has been materially softened during recent decades by the cumulative effect of three steps in the English procedure:

1. A much larger percentage of persons charged with crime is found "unfit to plead," that is, so mentally disordered at the time for trial that they are incompetent to conduct their defense and therefore to stand trial. The number has been rising, both relatively and absolutely. During the five years 1944-49, as many were found unfit to plead as were found mentally irresponsible at the time of the act. In Scotland, an even higher proportion are disposed of this way.[28] And while there is disagreement among psychiatrists whether this in-

competency involves a greater or lesser degree of mental disorder than inability to know the "nature and quality of the act" or that it was wrong, so as to render a person irresponsible under the M'Naghten test, the practical fact is that prison medical officers and other experts seem to construe the former concept more loosely, and to declare "unfit to plead" any person suffering from a certifiable form of mental disorder.

2. Although the wording of the M'Naghten rules remains unchanged, their application and interpretation are much more liberal today than even twenty or twenty-five years ago. It is difficult to generalize, because different trial judges vary in the extent to which they will take liberties with the traditional formula, and juries will vary in the extent to which they adhere to a strict instruction by one judge, or jump at an invitation to a broader view offered by another judge. But certainly some judges have offered the jury a very broad interpretation. The rule has even been stated liberally enough to make irresistible impulse a defense, although ostensibly this is not the law. Certainly in cases where there is no conflict about the fact that the defendant is seriously disordered, and prison medical officers and psychiatrists agree that the defendant is "insane" in a medical sense, the judge is not likely to require the jury to consider whether he literally meets the M'Naghten test. Thus Mr. Justice Humphries told the Royal Commission that in such a case, he tells the jury: "You have seen the man and the way he behaves and heard two witnesses who state the wild things that he did. Every-

body is of the opinion that he was insane and the doctor
has said he is. Consider your verdict."[29]

3. Perhaps the most important modification, and the
one that Americans are perhaps least likely to be cog-
nizant of, is the use of the Prerogative of Mercy, especially to reprieve murderers condemned to death. The
death sentence is mandatory in England on a conviction
of murder, but less than half of those so condemned are
actually executed. The Home Secretary reviews every
capital case before the law is allowed to take its course,
to determine whether there are grounds for advising the
Crown to commute the sentence to life imprisonment.
For the purpose of this review the Home Secretary has
before him not only all the material that was before the
trial court, but also a report on the prisoner's physical
and mental condition prepared by the prison medical
officer, and police reports including information about
the prisoner's character and antecedents. Where there
is reason to believe the prisoner to be insane, a medical
inquiry is held. If it appears that the prisoner is certi-
fiably insane—that is, suffering from a recognized form
of mental disorder of such severity that he is a proper
subject for hospitalization in a mental institution—the
practice is invariably to reprieve him. "It is not a question," said Sir John Anderson, "of how mad the person
is—a certificate by competent medical men that he is
insane is conclusive. I do not think the Home Secretary
ever seeks to go behind such a thing."[30]

While this practice is of long standing, the tendency
in recent years, especially since 1944, has been to hold

medical inquiries resulting in reprieves in a much larger percentage of the cases than was formerly the case.[31] This practice has the effect of reducing the M'Naghten rule to a much smaller area than would be true if it stood unalleviated by the prerogative function. While the pardoning power of the American governors is similar in nature, in no American state has that power been developed to anything like the extent of the British Prerogative of Mercy.

The cumulative effect of these three lines of development in England is to reduce the actual impact of the M'Naghten rule to a minimum. Half the cases are taken care of by the "unfit to plead" rule, where the measure of unfitness seems broadly to be certifiability. Then, in the actual trial where the M'Naghten rule controls, we find trial judges frequently giving it a very liberal interpretation. Then, if the defendant is found guilty of murder, in every case there is review by the Home Secretary, to decide whether to recommend commutation to life imprisonment, and here again the test is certifiability. The number of persons against whom the restrictiveness of the M'Naghten case really operates is therefore very small indeed.

The same factors also operate in varying degree in the American states. I have no statistics, but it is my impression that an increasing proportion of the cases are disposed of on a plea of mental unfitness to stand trial, instead of by the actual trial in which the disorder is raised as a defense. In New York, I understand this is now as prevalent a practice as in England; over half the cases are disposed of this way. This has the advantage of avoiding the expense and effort of a criminal trial, as well as the advantage of employing a less rigid and artificial legal test of "insanity." But it has certain disadvantages. Although the accused stands charged with a crime, the determination of his guilt or innocence is postponed until the time when, if ever, he is sane enough to stand trial. In the meantime, the crime stands on the books as unsolved, and the defendant has a charge hanging over his head. If recovery does not occur within a reasonably short time, it will probably be both impractical and unfair to try him—impractical because the prosecuting witnesses will have cooled or disappeared, unfair because the public may feel it undesirable and unjust to try a man years after the act, especially since the fact of his serious mental disorder at the time when he was first arraigned (serious enough to have required years of institutional care) indicates that he was probably also abnormal at the time of the act. It would therefore seem better to liberalize the test of irresponsibility and dispose of the criminal charge, rather than to keep an illiberal test, and then circumvent it by finding defendants unfit to plead. But if old rules are *not* revised to meet the felt needs of new times, administration will develop practices that evade or at least avoid application of the rules.

The search for a clear and certain rule in this field is a misguided one, a manifestation of the all-too-human yearning for certainty and order in an uncertain and chaotic world. We long for some mechanical rule of thumb—some gimmick—that will make a hard job easy. Perhaps this is part of a more pervasive craving for unquestioned standards and psychological security which Max Lerner has called "The most corroding development in the American character." It is a manifestation of that anthropomorphic view of the world that reads purpose and design into the workings of natural forces, and that leads ultimately to a picture of a rational universe governed by law. The great spread of scientific knowledge during recent times has produced no evidence that supports this picture. The evidence it has produced tells us the picture is false. We shall make progress faster when we abandon this delusion and proceed on the basis of what is ascertainable.

But if the yearning for certainty is not peculiar to law, it seems to be particularly strong with respect to law. There is a widespread feeling on the part of the public that the law ought to be clear and definite. Even lawyers share this feeling. Although they must know that all law is a good deal less definite than laymen suppose, lawyers make heroic efforts to maintain the illusion of certainty. When bar association leaders make speeches about the law, we rarely find them talking about the dynamic and adaptive character of law. Rather, they emphasize its antiquity and its unchanging permanence. This is what Jerome Frank called the basic myth of the law.[32] It is probably the product of some deep-seated irrational drives—but it is not for me to try to psychoanalyze the entire legal profession.

Stability in the law is important. But while law must be stable, yet, as Dean Pound said, "it cannot stand still . . . continual changes in the circumstances of social life demand continual new adjustments to the pressure of other social interests as well as to new modes of endangering security. Thus the legal order must be flexible as well as stable. It must be overhauled continually and refitted continually to the changes in the actual life which it is to govern."[33]

Stability is of much less importance in the criminal law governing insanity as a defense than it is in such fields as commercial and property law. No mentally disordered person consults the law before he kills someone to determine whether his disorder is such that he will be acquitted. In this field, we have no justification for demanding definite rules. Here as in so much of public law—of which criminal law is a part—the judge's function is not the humble one of applying fixed rules to fact situations, as the "slot machine" theory of the judicial function would have us believe. The judge, and the lawyers practicing before him, must exercise insight, judgment and resourcefulness in weighing the competing social interests that are involved in almost every case. Our really good judges have known this and have always acted on their knowledge; they used their wits and their social and political judgment in deciding whether precedents should be extended or restricted, and it is to their exercise of judgment that the common law owes its vitality and its capacity for growth.[34] "Much of the uncertainty of law is not an unfortunate accident; it is of immense social value."[35]

The spirit and tradition of our system of law does not call for establishing detailed formulations of specific "tests" of mental responsibility. Many of our most fundamental principles of criminal and of civil justice are expressed in broad phrases such as "due process," "unreasonable," "*mens rea.*" It is neither legally wise nor scientifically sound to try to reduce such principles to a body of detailed rules, inflexibly attaching fixed consequences to given sets of facts.

During the 19th century there was a tendency to reduce all law to a system of rigid rules. The M'Naghten rules are perhaps a manifestation of that tendency. But today we are not inclined to look upon law as a symmetrical body of hard and fast precepts imposed upon us in a bygone age, inexorably to be followed and to be handed on from generation to generation. More often, the law in the books gives us only an ideal and a technique—a general proposition expressing an ideal of reasonable and fair balancing of the interests of politically organized society and those of individual liberty, and a technique of legal reasoning for reaching that ideal. In such a system, precedents are important as illustrations of the technique, and also because continuity and symmetry in the law are among the social interests we want to protect. But the continuity must be the continuity of the ideals, and not of detailed rules. Changing social, economic or scientific data may require changes in the rules to maintain the ideal. We should not allow adherence to the rule in the face of changing data to make us lose sight of the ideal.

There is constant danger that we may do just that. The yearning for certainty is always with us, eager to seize upon the specific rule as the embodiment of and then as the substitute for the ideal. We must be constantly on guard not to allow this human weakness to ·stand in the way of the creative development of doctrines and principles adequate to the demands that will surely be made upon them in a dynamic and rapidly changing society.

"Existing rules and principles," said Judge Cardozo, "can give us our present location, our bearings, our latitude and longitude. The inn that shelters for the night is not the journey's end. The law, like the traveler, must be ready for the morrow. It must have a principle of growth."[36]

We have today reached the point where there is substantial agreement that the right-and-wrong test is outmoded and needs overhauling. In England, 11 of the 12 members of the Royal Commission on Capital Punishment agreed that "the test of responsibility laid down by the McNaghten Rules is so defective that the law on the subject ought to be changed."[37] In this country, all but one member of the American Law Institute's Criminal Law Advisory Committe likewise agreed that the M'Naghten formulation is inadequate.[38]

What I have been saying is therefore not original or new. We have today a clear consensus among those most qualified to judge that the law as it stands in most jurisdictions needs revision. If there is any justification for my having used so many words to restate that conclusion, André Gide has worded it for me. "Everything has been said already. But as no one listens, we must always begin again."

The question now is what to put in the old rule's stead. The next chapter discusses the main proposals that have been advanced—particularly Dr. Ray's solution as embodied in the law of New Hampshire and the District of Columbia, and the formulation of the Model Penal Code being drafted by the American Law Institute—and undertakes to answer the question: which is the better?

CHAPTER FOUR

Two Roads from M'Naghten

Thoughtful students of the subject have today largely come round to the view that the right-and-wrong test is not the clear and certain formula it was once supposed to be, and that certainty is at all events a wild goose that we may as well give up chasing. There is no clear and simple rule for making discriminations that are inherently complex and difficult.

Proponents of the right-and-wrong test themselves today largely accept this fact, and have made an interesting shift in their position. In place of the old argument that the traditional test is clear and definite, they now tell us that—rightly understood—it is broad enough to cover all the cases that should properly be covered. Or they say that in practice at least, it has proved flexible enough to permit juries to work rough justice in most cases. The most engagingly frank statement of this view is that of a British psychiatrist. "To put it in rather a bald way," he said, "the present rules are such nonsense in many cases that the people can exercise their own common sense, whereas with more precise rules more rigidly interpreted the ultimate effect would not be as good as the present one."[1]

But many and probably most of us would prefer Mr. Justice Frankfurter's position, that "If you find rules that are, broadly speaking, discredited by those who have to administer them . . . then I think the law serves its best interests by trying to be more honest about it . . . to have rules which cannot rationally be justified, except by a process of interpretation which distorts and often practically nullifies them . . . is not a desirable system. . . . I am a great believer in being as candid as possible about my institutions. They are in large measure abandoned in practice, and therefore I think the M'Naghten Rules are in large measure shams. That is a strong word, but I think the M'Naghten Rules are very difficult for conscientious people, and not difficult enough for people who say, 'We'll just juggle them.' "[2]

Once we accept the fact that the old test does not operate in fact as it purports to do, it is easier for us seriously to consider whether we should not adopt a more realistic rule. Two new developments give us reason to think we have perhaps reached that point. The first is the Durham case[3] in the District of Columbia, repudiating the traditional right-and-wrong and irresistible impulse tests, and adopting the product rule, that a defendant will be held irresponsible if his criminal act was the product of mental disease or defect. In England, the Royal Commission on Capital Punishment in 1953 recommended a somewhat similar rule.[4]

The second development is the Model Penal Code

which the American Law Institute has been drafting—
a herculean undertaking that has been in progress for a
number of years now. At the 1955 meeting of the Institute, tentative draft sections dealing with mental irresponsibility were discussed and approved.

Without laying claim to any prophetic vision, I nevertheless venture to predict that the future belongs to
these two alternatives. We are going to depart from the
M'Naghten test to try to find our way toward a rule
that better accords with modern psychiatric thinking.
The eminence of the staff and the committee that has
been working on the Model Penal Code and the quality
of their work has been such that that Code, when finally
promulgated, is certain to be accepted as the definitive
model for all criminal law reforms for years to come. It
is therefore important that its proposals be given the
careful study they deserve, and weighed against alternative solutions.

The Model Code's main provision dealing with mental
irresponsibility, as tentatively approved by the Institute,
reads as follows:

"A person is not responsible for criminal conduct if
at the time of such conduct as a result of mental disease
or defect he lacks substantial capacity either to appreciate the criminality of his conduct or to conform his
conduct to the requirements of law."[5]

This formulation does two things. First, although it
adheres to the essence of the right-and-wrong test, it
makes some important changes in wording. Second, it

supplements that test by adding a second, impairment of volitional capacity as a defense.

Most of the changes in wording are clearly improvements over the M'Naghten phrasing. The controversial word "know" is not used. Nor is "nature and quality of the act." Nor "wrong." Although volitional incapacity is recognized as a defense, it is not expressed in terms of "irresistible impulse." All those controversial old terms, whose meanings have been debated for a century, are discarded.

Perhaps the most important change in wording that the Code would make is the insertion of the word "substantial," so as to require only that the defendant lack "substantial" capacity to appreciate the criminality of his conduct or to conform to the requirements of the law. The M'Naghten rule, taken literally, seems to require *total* impairment of the cognitive faculty: the defendant must *not know*. The Code draftsmen are quite right in saying: "Nothing makes the inquiry into responsibility more unreal for the psychiatrist than the limitation of the issue to some ultimate extreme of total incapacity, when clinical experience reveals only a graded scale with marks along the way."[6]

That is psychiatrically sound. But what now becomes of that old argument for the right-and-wrong test, that it is necessary to give the jury a clear and definite rule? What becomes of the main objection to the New Hampshire rule, that it *fails* to give the jury any such definite guide as to what form or degree of mental disorder should be deemed sufficient to relieve from criminal responsibility? Introducing the loose word "substantial" into the formulation without defining it makes the rule as indefinite as any rule can be, for it gives the jury no clue as to where the line is to be drawn between a substantial lack of capacity and an insubstantial one. Some judges would probably want to define the word for the jury. But what could they say? Judge Gerald F. Flood of Philadelphia, in the discussion of this provision at the annual meeting of the American Law Institute, May 21, 1955, said that he would feel obliged to give the jury a definition, but that it would be a pretty difficult thing to do. He felt that he would eventually come up with a definition to the effect that a jury should find "substantial" lack of capacity if they find capacity so impaired that they do not feel the accused can justly be held responsible. He felt that he would prefer a formulation which would frankly state the rule in those words.[7]

The Model Code formula is a recognition that definiteness in this field is a mere *ignis fatuus*. The most significant and most hopeful thing about the Institute's formula is that a group of eminent lawyers have at long last recognized this fact, and are ready to stop chasing will-o'-the-wisps.

The Model Code formula would resolve one big ambiguity in the right-and-wrong test by abandoning the vague word "wrong" and substituting "criminality." Strangely enough, although 112 years have elapsed since the M'Naghten formula was laid down, and although it has been adopted as law in hundreds of cases, there is still no consensus as to just what "wrong" means, as used in the test. Specifically, does it mean morally wrong, or contrary to law?

As late as 1952, the English Court of Criminal Appeal had to wrestle with this question; it decided that the word meant legally wrong. In the same year, the High Court of Australia expressly refused to follow this interpretation and held instead that "wrong" meant morally wrong.[8] Mr. Justice Cardozo, writing the opinion in a leading American case, also held it meant moral wrong.[9] The same has been held in Scotland.[10] Most American cases have never bothered to explain in which sense they are using the word. The Code makes the criterion appreciation of the "criminality" of the act.

Standing alone, this change would have the effect of adopting the more restrictive of the two interpretations. It would condemn as responsible and fit for punishment some of the most wildly disordered persons ever seen— for example, paranoid persons with elaborately developed delusions, who hear "voices" and who kill believing that the deed is commanded by God. Such a person may be fully aware of the criminality of the act. He may even commit it precisely *because* he knows it is criminal: believing that he is the reincarnation of Jesus Christ, ordained again to suffer execution, he commits an act that will bring about that result.

The draftsmen of the Code agree that such a person should not be held responsible. But they believe he would be absolved by the second half of the test: he

would not have substantial capacity to conform his conduct to his knowledge of the act's criminality.[11]

But psychiatrists would apparently not all agree that
the "capacity to conform" concept covers these situations. Capacity to control is not the primary element in
the case of the paranoid person who kills someone under
delusion of divine command. To stretch it so as to make
it cover such cases would require the experts to go
through the same sort of mental gymnastics that they
now have to go through in trying to force cases into the
M'Naghten mold. I have asked a number of psychiatrists
throughout the country whether in their opinion these
situations would be covered by the Code formula. Some
said yes and some no. The defense would probably be
able to produce experts who would be willing so to
stretch it; the prosecution would produce other experts
who would say it could not be so stretched, and we
would have the same battle of experts that the present
rules produce.

The "capacity to conform" part of the Model Code
formula would broaden the insanity defense in most
states by accepting what the law has called "irresistible
impulse." That is now accepted as a defense in at least
fifteen states.[12] In some of these (Massachusetts, for example) it has been a part of the law for as long as the
right-and-wrong test. So the proposal to add it is hardly
a radical innovation, although it will no doubt be regarded as such by some lawyers and judges in the states
that have not accepted it.

If it is to be accepted, the Model Code's terminology

is again an improvement. "Irresistible impulse" is an unscientific term. It is perhaps another example of the 19th century penchant for using absolute terms as "rhetorical flourishes." In psychiatry, as in life generally, there are few absolutes. Strictly, as Dr. Robert Waelder has said, "irresistible" can be used in a well-defined way only of certain impulses that no human being can resist. The need to sleep, for example, becomes irresistible after a certain time. One man may be able to stay awake longer than another, but there is a point where the need to sleep cannot be conquered by anyone. But when we enter the area of impulses that are resisted by some people but not by others, and the psychiatrist is asked whether an urge that Tom and Dick have often felt but always successfully resisted was "irresistible" to Harry on a given occasion, there are no accepted criteria he can employ.[13]

In certain disorders the psychiatrist may be able to say there was utter inability to resist—for example, in the irrational acts of certain epileptics, paralytics and schizophrenics. But such conditions are rare. More common are impulses that are not absolutely irresistible, but that are nevertheless tremendously strong. The strongest kleptomaniac urge can probably be momentarily controlled while the person knows he is being watched. "The policeman at the elbow test" which some courts have employed for irresistible impulse,[14] would permit very few diagnoses of irresistible impulse. Cases that do come under this restricted concept would probably be so far out of touch with reality that they could also be said not to know the nature and quality of the act.

In Chapter II, I related the case of a young man in Lancaster, Pennsylvania, who, under terrific strain from pressures and resentments that had been building up within him for years, suddenly and without premeditation or motive killed a young woman he hardly knew. Was his condition such as to come within the legal notion of irresistible impulse? The answer will necessarily depend on how one interprets the phrase. Two psychiatrists may see eye to eye on the facts. Their clinical diagnosis may be the same. Both may agree that the patient was the victim of a tremendously strong urge to commit the act and that his power to resist was badly impaired. But one may testify that the impulse was not irresistible, and the other that it was, because he interprets the word "irresistible" in a more liberal way than the first. He reasons that, as in most such cases, the act was a crystallization, an explosive outburst of pressures that have been present in the person's mind for weeks and months or even years, building up until they exploded into action, and that this can therefore be called an irresistible impulse. The other interprets irresistible to mean absolutely irresistible, and he does not find that the act could be so described.

So long as we call on psychiatrists to answer questions employing categorical and unscientific absolutes, they will necessarily have to interpret those terms as best they can, and inevitably different psychiatrists will interpret them differently.

The second word in the phrase "irresistible impulse" has also been criticized. "Impulse" suggests an urge that is sudden and momentary. But this again is rare. More typically, the urge has been manifesting itself over a period of time, and has been building up in intensity.

The melancholia patient, for example, experiences a change of mood which alters his whole existence. He may believe that a future of such misery awaits both him and his family that death for all is the best way out. "The criminal act, in such circumstances, may be the reverse of impulsive. It may be coolly and carefully prepared; yet it is still the act of a madman. This is merely an illustration; similar states of mind are likely to lie behind the criminal act when murders are committed by persons suffering from schizophrenia or paranoid psychoses due to disease of the brain."[15]

To avoid some of the semantic difficulty that the phrase "irresistible impulse" raises, others beside the draftsmen of the A. L. I. Model Penal Code have suggested that the term be discarded and other phrasing substituted.[16] The Model Code's phrase, "capacity . . . to conform," is probably as satisfactory as any that can be found.

In recommending addition of this "capacity to conform" test, the draftsmen admit that: "The application of the principle will call, of course, for a distinction between incapacity upon the one hand, and mere indisposition on the other. Such a distinction is inevitable in the application of a standard addressed to impairment of volition. We believe that the distinction can be made."[17]

But in fact it is very difficult to make this distinction between incapacity and mere indisposition. Modern psychiatry conceives of practically every process of the personality as regulated by the interplay of excitatory and inhibitory forces. Every person is subject to a multitude of complex forces. Sometimes these are so delicately balanced that a very slight shift in the ratio of strength between the driving and the restraining forces will mean the difference between doing and not doing something. A slight increase in cathexis (the driving impulse) or a slight decrease in anti-cathexis when a person's finger is on the trigger may make the difference that means death and crime. Where does indisposition leave off and incapacity begin?

If criminal acts alleged to have been the result of impulse or compulsion were always clearly nonmotivated or autonomous, the application of the capacity-to-conform test would be easy. Nonmotivated behavior, the product of some internal compulsion, should certainly not be deemed the result of "criminal intent." Rather, it would be more like the behavior of a somnambulist or a person whose hand is involuntarily propelled by another person. The trouble is that most kleptomaniacs, pyromaniacs or persons acting under other compulsions do show motivation in much the same way as other criminals. They plan their activities in advance, they select places and means that will prevent their being detected, and they realize that if detected they will be arrested and punished. As a result, it is very difficult to draw the line between normal urges and temptations to which all of us are subject and those which are so pathological as to show lack of capacity to conform.

What is likely to happen is that the psychiatrist will find lack of capacity if neither he nor the patient is able to account for the criminal behavior in terms of motives which are current, popular, and sanctioned by the particular culture, or by the members of a particular group within a culture.[18] But even this is no simple criterion. For example, lack of economic need no doubt plays an important role in determining whether a person is labeled a kleptomaniac or a thief. To put it simply, the psychiatrist no less than the layman is likely to be influenced by the common sense reasoning: "This woman is rich and has no (economic) need to steal. Yet instead of buying it as she so easily could, she stole it. She must be crazy." This reasoning assumes that the behavior of normal persons committing property crimes is explainable in terms of economic needs—an assumption which Sutherland's study of *White Collar Crime*[19] shows to be untrue. By resting on this assumption we conclude that larcenous behavior in wealthy persons must be "compulsive." Implicit in this reasoning also is some tacit criterion of "need." Whether or not another person is in need depends upon our own viewpoint. A poor person might consider a middle-class person not to be in need and that his stealing must therefore be the result of a compulsion. A middle-class person, on the other hand, is likely to entertain this notion only as it refers to upper-class persons whose incomes far exceed his own. "If all psychiatrists were poverty stricken, the proportion of shoplifters called 'kleptomaniacs' probably would be much higher than it is."[20]

"Capacity to control" can be interpreted to require that a person have not merely capacity to prevent himself if he tried, but also capacity to *wish* to prevent himself, or capacity to appreciate or attend to considerations that might have led him to stop if he had been able to appreciate or attend to them; or capacity to weigh his murderous scheme except in an insane scale of ethical values. Will all the expert witnesses, and all the judges agree on one interpretation? I fear they will not.

I have devoted this much time to pointing out the broad terminology used in the formulation proposed by the Model Penal Code, and the conflicts of interpretation that it allows, *not* because I object to such indefiniteness. On the contrary, I am convinced that a clear and specific formula would be too rigid. Mental disorder manifests itself in too varied forms to permit any rigid and exclusive definition of what manifestations should exculpate from responsibility. I point out that these ambiguities inhere in the Model Code formulation because the reason the Code draftsmen give for rejecting the Product rule is that *it* is ambiguous. I shall discuss this objection later.

First, I want to mention that there are other provisions in the Model Code dealing with mental responsibility. One, highly relevant to our subject of the "test" formulation, provides:

(1) Evidence that the defendant suffered from a mental disease or defect shall be admissible whenever it is relevant to prove that the defendant did or did not have a state of mind which is an element of the offense.

This in effect accepts as a supplementary rule a formulation which Professor Keedy of Pennsylvania some forty years ago advocated as the sole test of responsibility.[21] In a sense, it is merely an application in cases of mental disorder of the general principle of our law that the state of mind with which a person commits a criminal act is important in determining not only whether he should be punished therefor, but also, if he is to be punished, how severely. If the mental state requisite to a given crime is absent, the crime has not been committed.

The principle has been accepted in a number of states to reduce murder from first degree to second. Where first degree murder requires deliberation and premeditation, and the defendant because of his mental condition actually did not deliberate or premeditate, it has been held that he cannot be convicted of first degree murder, even though he knew right from wrong and was otherwise sane within the meaning of the test of insanity. But if sound at all, the principle is not limited in application to reducing first degree murder to second degree, but logically extends to all crime requiring a specific or even general criminal intent. The rule therefore states a broad principle which might, if made much use of, largely supplant the other formulation. Just how much difference in results in given cases this rule would make as against the right-and-wrong or capacity-

to-conform test, has, so far as I know, never been carefully studied. If a man is charged with common law
murder or with robbery or rape, how much difference
would it make whether the test applied is appreciation
of the criminality of the act and capacity to conform to
the requirements of the law, or lack of the criminal intent required to constitute the crime? No one has as yet
offered any clear answer to this question.[22] I can only
suggest that if the principle is used to permit consideration of such effects of mental disease as diminishing
controls, causing marked impulsiveness in behavior or
heightening neurotic drives, it will allow juries better
to tailor verdicts to individual cases.

Still other provisions of the Model Code deal with the
procedure to be followed in cases where the defendant's
mental condition becomes an issue in the case. These
will be discussed in our next chapter. Here, our subject
is the substantive "test" adopted by the Model Code,
and its relative merits as compared with the product
rule.

As already said, the draftsmen of the Model Code
rejected the product rule primarily because that rule—
that an accused is not to be held responsible if his unlawful act was the "product" of mental disease or defect
—is ambiguous. The difficulty, they said, "inheres in the
ambiguity of 'product.'" That was the reason for rejecting the rule assigned in the printed draft. More recently,
a memorandum sent to members of the Institute's Criminal Law Advisory Committee advanced a second reason
—that "mental disease" is also ambiguous.

This would seem to indicate that the Code draftsmen want a rule that has greater certainty. Yet as we have seen they have practically abandoned the search for certainty by using the vague word "substantial"—as well as by using concepts of capacity for appreciation and for control which are incapable of measurement. Professor Wechsler, the reporter, wanted to go even further in that direction and leave it to the jury to say whether the defendant was so mentally incapacitated that he cannot "justly" be held responsible.[23] If there is a more ambiguous word than "substantial" it is "justly." It is with these ambiguities of the Model Code formulation in mind that we must consider the charge of ambiguity raised against the product rule.

First, the ambiguity of the term "mental disease." The argument runs as follows: Although "'mental disease" was a clear enough concept a hundred years ago when all such disease was thought to be the result of lesions in the brain, it is today a very vague concept. Especially is this true if we hold to the "quantitative" view, that there is an unbroken continuum from "normal" to "abnormal." But if "mental disease" has no clearly defined limits, how can that concept be used to sort out those who should be held irresponsible from the responsible? It is necessary to limit the term, for purposes of the criminal law, to "the severely abnormal group." And the way to define this group is by reference to capacity for knowledge and control.

We can agree with every part of this thesis except the conclusion. It is true that "mental disease" is a term that has no standard psychiatric meaning. I understand that Dr. Karl Menninger is now questioning even such "diagnostic categories of mental health" as have been more or less accepted. Even where two experts agree in their findings as to the facts, one may label the condition "mental disease" and another may not. There may even be some psychiatrists—although not very many—who would regard all criminals as mentally disturbed, and so would regard the fact of the crime as itself evidence of mental disease.

But this problem of defining mental disease is with us no matter what rule we adopt. We are dealing with the question when and to what extent mental disease or defect should relieve from criminal responsibility. To determine that, we must first ask whether this is a case of mental disease or defect at all, or whether the person is actually sane. Only if we find that there is mental disease or defect present do we come to the further question whether it is of such a kind or degree as should relieve from criminal responsibility. The right-and-wrong test asks whether at the time of the act the accused "was laboring under such a defect of reason, *from disease of the mind,* as not to know the nature and quality of the act," etc.

The Model Code asks whether as a result of mental disease or defect the defendant lacked substantial capacity to appreciate or to conform. The Product rule asks whether the act was the product of the disease or defect. All of them must meet the requirement of the existence of mental disease or defect. Where they differ is in their further requirements: the Code's two capacities, or the product concept.

The Code draftsmen, as already said, argue that mental disease is meaningful only in relation to the impairment of specific functional capacities, and that it is therefore psychiatrically sound to define criminal irresponsibility in terms of the two capacities that are relevant for the law's purposes—capacity to appreciate what one is doing and capacity to conform one's actions to such understanding.

But psychiatrists tell us that it is not true that mental disease is meaningful only in relation to the impairment of specific functional capacities. They tell us on the contrary that mental disease is an all-pervading and totally disorganizing state. The weakness of the attempt to delineate the nondeterrables in terms of capacity to appreciate the criminality of one's act and capacity to conform one's conduct to the requirements of law lies in the fact that these "capacities" are not psychiatric concepts. They are not part of the conceptology that the psychiatrist works with. No projective psychological tests that have been thus far developed are capable of measuring the specific capacity of an individual to appreciate the criminality of his conduct or the strength of his capacity for control. No one has even suggested a test or method for measuring these capacities. Psychiatry does not work with these concepts, and no research now going on is going to throw any light on them.[24]

The psychiatrist, if asked to delimit the "severely abnormal" would use wholly different methods. As Dr.

Guttmacher informed his fellow members on the A. L. I.
Criminal Law Advisory Committee—or tried to inform
them—the psychiatrist would identify the nondeterrables "by an analysis of their past social behavior and
by the use of projective psychological tests, such as the
Rorschach and Thematic Apperception Test, rather
than by any method of determining their knowledge of
right and wrong or the existence of an irresistible impulse. Their delinquency depends basically on the relative force of their antisocial drives and the strength and
quality of the superego. These factors are not necessarily
equated with the knowledge of right and wrong and the
existence or nonexistence of an irresistible impulse."[25]

The product rule, on the other hand, would not attempt to write into law *any* psychiatric dogma, no matter how sound it may appear today. It would not define
mental disease or defect, but would leave the law free to
incorporate new content into those terms with the
advance of scientific knowledge. Nor would it dictate to
the psychiatrist any artificial formula for determining
whether the act was the product of the disease or defect.
And when we are dealing with as dynamic and rapidly
changing a science as psychiatry, isn't it better *not* to
write into static law any dogmatic concepts?

Consider for a moment how rapidly scientific knowledge is growing in our day. Modern science has given us
a new world. And what is most new about it is the very
prevalence of newness, the changing scale and scope of
change itself, so that as J. Robert Oppenheimer said,
"the world alters as we walk in it, so that the years of a

man's life measure not some small growth or rearrangement or moderation of what he learned in childhood, but a great upheaval."

Nowhere has that upheaval, that speed-up in the metabolism of science, been greater than in psychiatry. Tremendous advances have been made since Freud developed the psychoanalytic method. "The psychiatrist of half a century ago . . . would be hopelessly lost and confused in a modern psychiatric clinic . . . . the whole concept of mental health and mental disorder has been revolutionized."[26]

The newest developments lie not so much in psychoanalysis as in biochemistry and neurophysiology. "Wonder drugs" are performing their wonders in mental no less than physical illnesses.

Penicillin has been found to be effective to kill the spirochetes of syphilis in the brain. As a result, first admissions to New York city and state hospitals because of general paresis declined about 50 percent in the five years from 1946 to 1951. Insulin can relieve perhaps 70 percent of the victims of schizophrenia, the most common and most tragic form of psychosis, if they are treated within the first three months of an attack. Pellagra has been practically eliminated in mental hospitals of the South as a result of the discovery that niacin cures pellagra. At an Institute in Psychiatry and Neurology I participated in recently, we had a report on tests that had been made of the effectiveness of two newer drugs, Chlorpromazine and Reserpine. Both promise to give excellent results in reintegrating schizophrenic dis-

orientation. An International Colloquium on Chlorpromazine was held in Paris late in 1955. Derivatives of
rauwolfia have given helpful results against various
forms of mental illness, including mental deficiency,
according to reports from Modesto State Hospital,
California.[27] For patients who need not sedation but the
opposite kind of treatment—that is, who need to be lifted
out of a severe depression—Meratran, another new
drug, is showing great promise. Even newer drugs are
in the offing. We have probably seen only the beginning
of a study of pharmacological means of sedation and
antispasmodic medication to help people deal with their
tensions.

Some medical men still have doubts about possible
deleterious side effects of these drugs. Caution is of
course proper, but we have now had sufficient experience with them to lead at least one psychiatric clinic
director to say that to deny these drugs to patients in
state institutions for whom no other effective therapy is
practicable is nothing less than malpractice.

Epilepsy, formerly deemed incurable, has now been
shown by neurological research to be a disorder of the
energy and economy of brain cells, which can be controlled by increasingly efficient chemical drugs such as
Tridione and Dilantin and sometimes by brain surgery.
As a result, 80 percent of all epileptics can now lead
normal lives.

Electric shock therapy can remedy a severe mental
depression and help people suffering from certain types
of schizophrenia. Interesting experiments are also under

way to determine whether chemical agents in the body, such as lysergic acid diethylmamide, nicknamed "LSD25", may be a cause of clinical schizophrenia.

In recent years we have learned that there is a close relationship between the amount of sugar present in a person's blood and his social behavior. A fairly long list of aggressive crimes may be committed either under the influence of insulin or in a state of spontaneous hypoglycemia (the medical term for a decrease in the normal amount of sugar in the blood). The lower the sugar level falls the greater is the tendency to commit crime. Lack of calcium also seems to produce antisocial attitudes and actions. "Many high strung, very emotionally unstable individuals are victims of calcium starvation . . . . The calcium-starved personality is always on edge. At home, a harsh word from any member of the family, at the table, for instance, would result in a plate or knife or some other utensil being hurled at the aggressor. In school a blow, a shout, or a curse would be hurled at a fellow student, or even at a teacher."[28]

Studies are also being pursued of the relationship between endocrine gland activity and aggressive and antisocial behavior. The endocrine glands, through their hormones, influence personality by their effects on all parts of the body, particularly the brain and nervous system. One of the glandular secretions, thyroxin, increases excitability and nervousness, while the lack of it produces sluggishness in thinking and acting. A lack of parathyrin causes an increase in sensitivity and irritability. Cretinism, a type of dwarfism and imbecility developing during fetal life or early infancy as a result of thyroid deficiency, can now be successfully treated with thyroid if recognized early enough.

Dr. Edward Podolsky, in a recent article with the vivid title, "The Chemical Brew of Criminal Behavior,"[29] tells of a study of inmates at Sing Sing Prison several years ago. It was found that robbers and burglars usually lacked pituitrin and parathyrin in their body chemistry. The same was true of those convicted of grand larceny, but these showed in addition an increase in thyroxin and thymus hormones. Murderers usually showed a decrease in the amount of parathyrin, but an abnormal increase in thymus, adrenalin and thyroxin. The great majority of all these prisoners had an excessive amount of non-protein nitrogen in their blood; their blood sugar level was low; their uric acid and cholesterol levels were always above normal.

This sort of biochemical evaluation of the criminal personality is still in its infancy. It may, in the near future, become an important methodology.

The use of drugs and other new methods have already largely displaced what to the public is also still a very new technique, the surgical operation called lobotomy. This is the cutting of portions of the prefrontal lobes of brain. These lobes are the part of the brain that is markedly larger in man than in any lower animals. They are what distinguish a highbrow from a lowbrow. Yet separation of this front part produces neither loss of sensation nor motor paralysis. It does, however, produce some change in personality, usually in the direction of making the person more docile. This has permitted the operation to be used to enable thousands of persons previously classed as incurable to be released from mental institutions; but it has also given some serious thinkers nightmares of some Big Brother of the future using it wholesale to enslave an entire population. Brain specialists still do not fully understand the functioning of the lobes. In some way they seem to control the balance between action and restraint. The significance of this balance for both mental disorder and crime is obvious, and while, as said, lobotomy is already falling into disuse, further research may have the profoundest importance for both psychiatry and criminal law.

Other new developments may also throw significant light on the subject. For example, it is now known that crimes of impulsive violence are committed mostly by young persons whose electrical brain waves, as measured by the electroencephalograph, show a defect in normal brain maturation for their age. Of repeated offenders, 34 percent had abnormal electroencephalograms.[30]

As a result of the use of drugs and other new methods, the mental hospitals are able today to cure and release a large percentage of their cases after only a few months of treatment. This too may have important repercussions in the law.[31] As the mental hospital becomes an instrumentality of positive health, instead of an "asylum" where unfortunates are "put away" almost certainly for life, we may develop a popular sentiment of enthusiasm and pride that will give positive support to their work. We have seen the same thing happen with the general hospitals. A century ago, hospitals were places devoted at best to the relief of suffering *in extremis*. As scientific research enabled them to become instrumentalities for cure, and not merely for palliatives and pity, hospitals became enthusiastically appreciated and widely used. But the psychiatric institutions until now have not shared in this popular sentiment. Few neighborhoods could point to neighbors home from the mental hospital with a new lease on life, new vigor and new constructive effectiveness. Hospitalization was a shameful matter to be kept secret and not to be talked about. Support for mental hospitals was motivated by pity and by waves of shame at exposures of their inadequacy, not by pride and enthusiasm. But now, with the mental institutions releasing their patients within less than one year, we may find the history of the general hospitals repeating itself.[32]

In view of these rapid developments, it takes a large dose of complacency to be willing to set down a rigid legal test of mental irresponsibility without worrying whether it may not be rendered scientifically obsolete within a year or two. It is one of the strengths, and not a weakness, of the Durham case rule that it would rely more on a dynamic and changing medical concept of mental disease than on a rigid and static legal "test." If the study of evolution and of individual growth teaches us anything at all, it should teach us that the flexibility inherent in man must be reflected in his law. "There must, so to speak, reside in the morals and the law an inner principle of adaptation, a *readiness to move* as new evidence comes in and as new aspects of human nature speak up for recognition."[33]

Any rule on this subject must take into account not only how easily the jury can understand and apply it when they are given their instructions and told to consider their verdict, but also how it will operate during the trial—especially how it will be applied in the examination and cross-examination of expert witnesses. Under a legal rule that requires substantial impairment of capacity to appreciate criminality or to conform, all the old questions that psychiatrists object to would still be as popular as ever. The experts would still be forced to testify not in terms of mental disorder with which they are familiar, but in terms of artificially isolated capacities for social conformity about which they have no special claim to knowledge. Any lawyer can foresee how the prosecutor, cross-examining a defense expert, would try to isolate capacity to appreciate the criminality of the act, for example, and force an admission that the accused knew that the act was criminal. As we have already said, on a superficial level the great majority of disordered defendants will know that the act was criminal, and so an admission to that effect will probably not be too hard to obtain from the witness. The distinction between knowing and appreciating the prosecutor may try to minimize or ignore, and argue to the jury that since the defendant's own experts themselves conceded that his capacity to know the criminality of the act was not impaired, he is responsible under the law.

The cases with which there is the most difficulty are

the more severe character disorders—the so-called psychopaths and severe character neurotics. There is no agreement among psychiatrists as to whether any of these should be included within the term "mental disease." In fact they prefer not to use the term at all. They talk of "syndromes" and "reaction patterns," and use the general term "disorder"; but rarely "disease."

Dr. Robert Waelder says that outside a central core of conditions in which the sense of reality is crudely impaired and inaccessible to the corrective influence of experience—for example, organic psychoses, schizophrenia, and manic-depressive psychoses, in which the patients are confused or disoriented or suffer from hallucinations or delusions—outside these, there is a fringe area of conditions which may, or may not. be considered diseases of the mind, and among these he includes psychopathies. "Whether or not a psychiatrist is willing to classify any one of these conditions as diseases of the mind," says Dr. Waelder, "depends more on his philosophy than on any factual question that can be settled by observation and reasoning."[34]

Dr. Manfred Guttmacher of Baltimore has said the same:

> There is certain to be professional disagreement as to whether some of these cases should be classified as psychotic (schizophrenic) or psychopathic (schizoid psychopaths). The training and orientation of the psychiatrist is likely to be the decisive factor. If his orientation is psychoanalytic, he will be more likely to consider cases with severe character disorders as suffering from a mental disease.[35]

In a round-table discussion of this subject at the University of Chicago, Dr. Addison M. Duval, Assistant Superintendent of St. Elizabeth's Hospital, reported that after the Durham case came down, the hospital staff held consultations and agreed that "sociopathic personality disturbance" (which is the psychiatrists' current term to replace "psychopathic personality") should not be regarded as mental disease within the meaning of the new rule. The lawyers present lifted an eyebrow at this. It seemed to them to demonstrate how completely under this new rule the law has abdicated in favor of the psychiatrists, even allowing them to decide in their own informal huddles what kinds of mental cases shall be deemed to come within the rule and what not.

The Model Code draftsmen, fearing that other psychiatrists would take the opposite view from that of the St. Elizabeth's staff, objected to the product rule particularly because it would operate to relieve the psychopaths of criminal responsibility. Since psychopathic personality is presently defined largely in terms of the very phenomenon that it purports to explain—that is, a disposition to the commission of criminal and other antisocial acts—if the expert classified a person as a psychopathic personality, he would almost necessarily have to say that the act was the product of the psychopathy. Yet many psychiatrists say that science today is not able to effect any "cure" for these persons, and that they may as well be confined in a prison as in a mental hospital, where they would only be a source of trouble. Paul Tappan has repeatedly said that channelling psy-

chopaths into mental hospitals instead of into prisons
is more likely to convert the hospitals into prisons than
to do the psychopaths any good.[36] The Model Code
therefore adds a specific—though I think ineffectively
worded—provision intended to exclude psychopaths
from being held irresponsible.[37]

We can sympathize with those who take this view,
especially if they are hospital administrators. But must
we bow to it? Dr. Hervey Cleckley, in his *Mask of
Sanity*, maintains that the psychopath *has* a mental disease and is less responsible for his behavior than many
psychotics. Many psychiatrists, especially the more ana-
lytically oriented, take essentially the same view. The
very fact that "psychopathic personality" is a waste-
basket classification, used in different senses by different
psychiatrists (and not used at all in current official nomenclature), suggests the unwisdom of a blanket exclu-
sion. If psychopaths are excluded from the category of
mental disease by legal fiat, what will happen, as the
Solicitor General of the United States has suggested,
is that there will be a tendency first to make a judgment as to what is the wise and fair disposition of the
individual case and then to announce a classification
accordingly, and not the other way about. "Attempting
to categorize cases as a matter of law according to these
vague distinctions would only complicate the difficulty.
Not an unbending rule, but enlightened understanding
of the special facts of each case should be our aim, especially where there is a broad twilight zone."[38]

Even the practical consequences of recognizing psychopathic personality as mental disease would probably not be overwhelming. If enough psychopaths are found irresponsible, we might find it practical to build separate institutions for them, which is probably the best solution. If one state cannot afford to do so, we could do so by interstate co-operation. The Western Interstate Commission for Higher Education is working on such a project now.

Even without such special institutions, if more psychopaths are sent to our ordinary mental hospitals, an adjustment in hospital organization could probably be made whereby they could be segregated. And having them in the hospital should, as Dr. Guttmacher has said, stimulate increased research on the behavior disorders, which have thus far been treated as psychiatry's step-children.

The research that is even now going on gives no reason to think that the problem is insoluble. Only recently at a meeting of the American Penal Congress, a Canadian neurologist reported experiments which indicate that certain characteristic brain-wave patterns, such as those found in epilepsy, are found among psychopaths. Other investigators are exploring the thesis that psychopathy is a kind of defense against schizophrenia. Both disorders seem to arise out of affection starvation. The schizophrenia victim reacts by developing withdrawal symptoms. The psychopath, instead, *acts out* his isolation and lack of warmth towards others. In various research centers, workers say that they have clues and hints which if pursued, may lead to fuller understand-

ing of the psychopath. Even now, on a merely empirical
basis, there would probably be a surprising degree of
agreement among psychiatrists as to which ones out of a
given group of psychopaths ought to be held irresponsible.[39]

If the consensus among psychiatrists is that psychopathic personality is at least in part a mental disease or
disorder, they should not allow practical problems of
administration to deter them from saying so, loudly and
clearly. In the long run, they will probably be doing us
a favor if they make us recognize the fact and make us
do something about it.

By refusing to recognize the psychopath as a mental
case, the Model Code formula refuses to come to grips
with what is in fact the most important group of abnormal criminals. These are the people who commit probably the major part of our violent crimes.[40] To regard
them as sane is in effect to pretend that the problem is
not a psychiatric one. I suggest that on the contrary it
is probably the most pressing psychiatric problem that
the criminal law must face, and I suggest that we proceed to face it now.

A second main charge of ambiguity lodged against the
product rule centers on the term "product." Opponents
say that this "product" concept is also hopelessly ambiguous.

The term product implies a "causal connection," as
the court in the Durham case indicated. And causation,
as every lawyer knows, is a formidable source of difficulty.

At the most elementary level, we have the basic question, does the rule mean that the disorder must have been *the* cause of the act, or merely one cause? To a philosopher, cause has a fairly simple meaning. One fact or event is the cause of another when the existence of the first is necessary to the existence of the second. In this sense, there may be and usually are a great many causes for every fact or event.

But in law, we have learned after long wrestling with the problem that although we use the same word, causation as the lawyer uses it is a wholly different concept from the philosopher's or the scientist's. In law, we usually concern ourselves only with the more or less direct causes of events, with what we call proximate cause. And we have learned that that concept can be used intelligently only by recognizing that what is proximate depends upon the point of view or purpose behind the inquiry. If the question is, what caused a certain individual to commit a given act, a medical man would be inclined to single out that factor that he would deal with, by application of his special knowledge and skills, if he were seeking to cure or prevent a repetition of the occurrence. But a sociologist might attribute as cause the social phenomenon that *he* would work on if *he* were called upon. One man's cause may be another man's incidental.

An even greater difficulty is involved when we try to trace causation from mental disorder to criminal conduct. As Dr. Philip Q. Roche has said, "Mental illness does not cause one to commit a crime nor does mental illness produce a crime. Behavior and mental illness are inseparable—one and the same thing."[41]

"The newborn infant comes into the world today precisely the same asocial little animal that he was when he was born to prehistoric man. By training and by example, a character metamorphosis, as amazing as physical maturation, occurs in a few scant years."[42] This conditioning is designed to give the child, in Dr. Roche's words, "a built-in, automatic set of optimal controls of his primary instincts sufficient for the usual stresses of social life."[43] Criminality and mental illness are evidence of the insufficiency or breakdown of those controls. Both are indicative of a losing struggle to maintain a controlled relationship with the social environment. Both are products of an inner conflict. Neither "causes" one to do wrong; they are both processes reflecting the breakdown of psychic controls and the release of latent antisocial drives common to us all. One man resolves the conflict by acting out in crime, another by living out in mental illness. The mentally ill person who commits a crime is cursed with a double failure of adaptation.

How then is the jury to find any answer to the question whether the mental disorder produced the crime? A preliminary aspect of that question is this one—are the medical witnesses to be allowed to testify to an opinion on this question of causation, or are they to be restricted to giving only a medical diagnosis? Psychiatrists have frequently criticised the older tests on the ground that they force the expert to answer questions that are beyond their medical expertise. Whether the

defendant knew right from wrong, for example, psychiatrists regard as a question of ethics, not psychiatry. The
Durham case repudiation of that test was in part a response to that criticism. But under the new test is the
psychiatric witness to testify only to his medical diagnosis? Judge Brosman of the U. S. Court of Military
Appeals suggested what seems a good reason for not so
limiting expert testimony.

"In light," he said in an important case, "of the
esoteric nomenclature used in the field, and the hyper-
technical divergence between various schools of psychiatric thought, as well as because of the complexity and
sheer uncertainty of the area under exploration, it can
readily be imagined what wholesale want of enlighten-
ment would eventuate from *purely* medical testimony
from the witness-psychiatrist."[44]

That scientific judgment as to the causal connection
between the disorder and the act will be difficult is no
reason for not asking the expert's opinion. The jury is
going to have to decide that issue, and we should give
them the benefit of any light the experts may be able to
give them.

But scientific men are by training cautious in their
hypotheses. They know that these hypotheses may be
proved wrong by later research. If the psychiatric witnesses are to be asked whether the act was the product of
the disorder, will they venture an opinion, or will most
of them refuse to make a definite commitment, or even
to speculate on probabilities? In some cases, the doctor
will perhaps feel fairly certain that an intimate connec-

tion existed between the clinical act and the illness, and
be able to demonstrate to the jury his reasons for his
judgment. In others, this will not be possible without
careful and lengthy study. But at least the doctor will be
able to present relevant facts in a psychiatrically realistic
way, instead of being asked to focus on artificially isolated "capacities." He will be able to give his diagnosis,
state the disorder the defendant suffers from, if any, its
usual symptoms and characteristics, and the extent to
which it seems to have affected this particular defendant's behavior, judgment and self control. Where the
crime was a serious and shocking one, and the person
has a major psychosis, the presumption that the act was
the product of the disorder would probably seem very
strong to any but a very rigid and biased psychiatrist.[45]

As a matter of fact the problem of proving a causal
connection is not essentially different in this disorder-
and-crime situation than in others. How can we ever
prove causation? We don't; instead, we present the raw
factual material and then try to induce the state of mind
in the judge or jury that will prompt him or them to say
that the relationship of cause and effect exists. How can
they be convinced? Only by their matching the raw facts
presented to them against their own background of
experience. We ask them for their estimate—their guess,
if you please—as to whether, on the basis of their established observations, a causal connection exists. Their
answer must come out of that background. It cannot be
derived by logic.

When the experience of the trier of the issue does not

supply the necessary background to make an informed guess, the party must present expert testimony. The function of the expert witness is to supply the items of information that are missing from the trier's experience background. It is not his function to make a conclusive evaluation of the causal relation in the case at hand. In practice, he will in many cases be willing to give an opinion as to whether such a causal connection existed. But his conclusion is only advisory. It is the trier who must ultimately make the determination whether or not the relationship between A and B is so close that B should be said to be the product of A. And his conclusion on that question may justifiably differ from the expert's judgment. For the scientific expert may, in accordance with his training, be very cautious in concluding that a causal relationship exists which he cannot demonstrate by scientific proof. But the law cannot wait for scientific proof. It must settle controversies as they arise, and so it is forced to act on probabilities. And as we have already said, the law's purpose may differ from that of medicine, and a conclusion that a causal connection exists may be justified for the purposes of the law, although for medical purposes it may not be.

Like so many others, this problem is in part semantic. The word "cause" calls up a whole body of legal material. To some extent, we can perhaps circumvent it by choosing a word with less legal philosophizing behind it. The Group for the Advancement of Psychiatry, in a very valuable report issued in 1955, proposed a rule that would read:

"No person may be convicted of any criminal charge when at the time he committed the act with which he is charged he was suffering with mental illness . . . and in consequence thereof, he committed the act."[46]

"Consequence" is a legally colorless word, and for that reason may be preferable to "product."

If we can disabuse ourselves of the idea that any clear and definite test of "insanity" is either possible or desirable, we can perhaps reconcile ourselves to the idea that what we really want is the jury's sense of justice. We recognize insanity as a defense not because it fits in logically; if we wanted logic, we'd use a different test— "intent" or amenability to punishment.[47] We are seeking not psychological precision, but the jury's judgment in the light of an adequate picture of his mental condition, as to whether the defendant should justly be held responsible and so punishable.

And the best device to get the jury's informed sense of justice, is the product rule. Under that rule, as the court in the Durham case in effect said, the jury will be expected to apply the requirement of causal connection in such a way as to carry out its traditional function of expressing the community judgment on the justice of the case. "Juries," said the court, "will continue to make moral judgments, still operating under the fundamental precept that 'Our collective conscience does not allow punishment where it cannot impose blame.' But in making such judgments, they will be guided by wider horizons of knowledge concerning mental life."

It has been objected that the "product" formula does

not put that responsibility to the jury clearly and frankly. Instead it obscures it by inviting the jury to explore the metaphysical problem of causation. We could put it to them more frankly by asking whether the accused was suffering from mental disease or defect "to such a degree that he ought not to be held responsible." That is the rule recommended by the Royal Commission. Or by the formula that the A. L. I. Reporter favored, "A person is not responsible for criminal conduct if as a result of mental disease or defect his capacity either to appreciate the criminality of his conduct or to conform his conduct to the requirements of law is so substantially impaired that he cannot justly be held responsible."

This was not accepted by the Institute. It seems less desirable than the Royal Commission wording in that it does not seem well designed to do what it purports to do. It purports to leave the issue of responsibility to the jury's sense of justice. Actually, however, it keeps the old right and wrong test plus the irresistible impulse test (liberalized by a new phrasing—impairment of capacity to appreciate criminality or to conform conduct to the requirements of law) and allows the jury to use its sense of justice only in deciding whether either of these capacities have been "so substantially impaired that he cannot justly be held responsible." But this still focuses attention on two artificially abstracted symptoms of mental disorder, instead of emphasizing the unitary nature of human personality and the pervasive effects of any disorder on that personality.

The product rule, or the Royal Commission's recommendation, would focus the issue and therefore the testimony on mental disorder, and not on unrealistically isolated symptoms of disorder. The Model Penal Code, instead, undertakes to give the jury a binding rule of *law* for determining the question, a rule that states as a matter of law what manifestations or symptoms of mental disorder the defendant must exhibit before the disorder will relieve from responsibility.

And while the Royal Commission formula would be franker, there is something to be said for calling for some causal connection between the disorder and the crime. There may be cases where the defendant was fairly certainly suffering from mental disorder, but where that disorder had nothing to do with the crime. A British doctor mentions a patient of his who heard imaginary voices. He broke into and entered a shop, not because of the promptings of his imaginary voices but because of the promptings of some very real and very undesirable associates.[48]

The Royal Commission itself agreed that:

Mental abnormalities vary infinitely in their nature and intensity and in their effects on the character and conduct of those who suffer from them. Where a person suffering from a mental abnormality commits a crime, there must always be some likelihood that the abnormality has played some part in the causation of the crime; and, generally speaking, the graver the abnormality and the more serious the crime, the more probable it must be that there is a causal connection between them. But the closeness of this connection will be shown by the facts brought in evidence in individual cases and cannot be decided on the basis of any general medical principle.[49]

Without in the least minimizing the difficulty of determining whether a criminal act was or was not the "product" of mental disease, it is necessary again to remind ourselves that the choice is not between a rule that is difficult to administer and one that is simple and easy. There is no simple, easy rule. And it is significant that the psychiatrists who will have to give the opinion— including the psychiatrists on the A. L. I.'s own criminal law advisory committee—do not consider it any more difficult to express an opinion on the causal relationship than on the questions of capacity to appreciate the criminality of the act or capacity to conform.

In formulating a new Model Penal Code, the A. L. I. faced somewhat the problem that the management of an industrial plant might face. The plant is more than a hundred years old. It has been and is depreciating. The question is whether there is still enough useful life left in it to be worth spending more repair and maintenance work on it, or whether the time has come to junk it. The drafstmen of the Code felt that the right-and-wrong test and the irresistible-impulse test have still enough usefulness that they are worth refurbishing. But a hundred years is a long time, for an industrial plant or for a legal concept that must rest on psychiatric foundations.

I do not believe that the defects of the right-and-wrong test can be patched up by adding capacity to conform. Both tests rest on the same outdated psychological assumption that "mind" is divisible into neatly separate functions, each operating independently of the other; that a person may have will power without understanding, or understanding without will power. Today we know that personality is single. Our mental processes are interdependent and interrelated, and mental disorder affects all these processes. Psychiatry has long ago moved beyond the point where either apprehension of criminality or capacity to conform can be treated as independent functions.

The glaring defect in the traditional legal rules governing "insanity" as a defense is that although they deal with a subject where the law must rest on psychiatric premises, the psychiatrists are convinced that the law's premises are unsound. If we are going to have a revision of the legal rule, we ought to adopt one that will stand up when examined in the light of the best current information and insights that psychiatry can give us, one that will bridge the gap that now exists between legal and psychiatric thinking. The Model Penal Code provisions fail to bridge that gap. They do not have the endorsement of the psychiatric profession, not even of the Institute's own psychiatric advisers.

It would be presumptuous and arrogant for me thus to set myself against the eminent authorities who drafted the Model Code, if I stood alone. But I do not stand alone, and those authorities do not stand together. All three of the psychiatrists who were placed on the advisory committee would prefer the product rule to the formulation adopted.

In 1955, I took an informal poll of mental hospital administrators attending the Seventh Annual Institute of Psychiatry and Neurology at Little Rock. Of twenty-six who expressed a preference, twenty-four favored the Durham case rule over the traditional legal tests. This is also the preference of most other psychiatrists who have expressed an opinion, both in this country and in Canada.[50]

Eminent lawyers have also taken this side of the argument. In 1942, the redactors of the Louisiana criminal law sought to adopt essentially the same rule, but the proposal was rejected. In Illinois twenty years ago the State Bar Association and the Cook County Judicial Council also urged such a rule.[51] New Hampshire has operated under this rule for eighty-five years.

I believe the future belongs to this rule. The American Law Institute's project for a Model Penal Code is a tremendous undertaking, being carried on by the most eminently qualified legal scholars in the country. What they propose will carry very great weight. It is to be hoped that before the Code is finally promulgated they will give further thought to the mental responsibility sections, and give the product rule the consideration it deserves.

CHAPTER FIVE

The Model Penal Code's Procedural Reforms[1]

As Mr. Justice Holmes more than once reminded us, Anglo-American law approaches all questions of substantive right through the avenue of procedure. This is largely true of the "insanity" issue in criminal cases. And it is becoming more true than it has been. Criminal procedure had its origins in a day when the accused was denied counsel. Today he has a constitutional right to counsel, even if he is indigent. We can be more technical today, and we are.

Perhaps illustrating the trend toward greater procedural detail is the fact that of the nine sections in the American Law Institute's Model Penal Code dealing with mental responsibility, three lay down substantive rules while six deal with procedure and rules of evidence. Thus far I have discussed only the substantive formulations of the "test" of criminal responsibility. But the procedure for determining that issue, and for determining the issue of mental competency to stand trial, is no less important.

BURDEN OF PROOF

Whether the defense of mental irresponsibility is one that the defendant must prove by a preponderance of evidence, or whether it is an ordinary defense which, once the issue is raised, the prosecution must disprove beyond a reasonable doubt, is a question on which the courts of the several states are almost exactly evenly divided.[2] The draftsmen of the Model Code therefore left open the question of which rule to adopt. The May, 1955, meeting of the Institute adopted the view that this is an ordinary defense, on which the prosecution has the ultimate burden of conviction.

On a question about which there has been such even division of opinion, it would be presumptuous to be dogmatic. Basically, how the burden should be allocated is a matter of public policy, involving underlying assumptions and attitudes concerning the concept of "guilt," political prejudices concerning the relative values and demands of individuals freedom and public safety, the availability of institutional and other facilities, and other factors.

Since it is rarely possible to provide conclusive scientific proof that the defendant's mental condition was such as to bring him within any recognized legal "test" of irresponsibility—whether that test be inability to know right from wrong, or substantial incapacity to appreciate the criminality of the act, or irresistible impulse, or whether the act was the "product" of the disorder—and since the jury must always decide on a balance of probabilities, the question of who has the burden of proof may be determinative.

On balance, the Institute's choice seems the preferable rule. Scientifically, at least where mental disorder is proved and where the crime is a serious and largely unmotivated one, the presumption should be that the act was the product of the disorder, and the burden should be on the prosecution to show that in the instant case the defendant, though disordered, was nevertheless responsible.[3]

In legal theory also, this rule is the one more in accord with current thinking. The opposite rule stems from the Opinion in M'Naghten's case,[4] which said that every man is to be presumed sane and responsible until the contrary is proved to the jury's satisfaction, and that the defense must be "clearly proved." (Today most of the American states that put the burden on the defendant no longer say that the defense must be "clearly" proved. Even the phrase "to the satisfaction of the jury" is losing popularity, the preferred formula today being that the defense must be proved by the preponderance of the evidence.[5]) In 1843, when the Opinion in M'Naghten's case was delivered, it was probably the rule that the defendant had the burden of "clearly" proving *all* affirmative defenses. "An acquaintance with legal history disposes one to think that had the judges been asked in 1843 where the burden lay of establishing circumstances of necessity or accident when a homicide was proved, they would have answered in similar words, that it must be clearly proved that at the time of committing the act the accused acted in self defence or caused the death by accident."[6] Today, the law is that where the defense is accident, the prosecution must establish beyond a reasonable doubt that the prisoner killed the deceased with malicious intention.

As Professor McCormick has said, ". . . as to all these claims for exoneration their truth goes in final analysis to the guilt—to the rightness of punishing the accused. Thus it seems inconsistent to demand as to some elements of guilt, such as an act of killing, that the jury be convinced beyond a reasonable doubt, and as to others, such as duress or capacity to know right from wrong, the jury may convict though they have such doubt."[7]

One specific point may be worth noting, however. Under the Code, the prosecution is not required to disprove an affirmative defense "unless and until there is evidence supporting such defense."[8] In most states which put the ultimate burden on the prosecution to prove mental responsibility, no disproof is required until and unless the defense presents evidence *sufficient to raise a reasonable doubt*.[9] In the District of Columbia, however, the Court of Appeals has said that "some evidence" is sufficient to overcome the presumption of sanity and to throw the burden on the prosecution to prove sanity beyond a reasonable doubt.[10]

The failure in the Model Code to state how strong the "evidence" supporting the defense must be in order to shift the burden to the prosecution was deliberate. "The Council of the Institute thought it the wiser

course to leave this question to the courts."[11] The only
alternatives that seem specifically to have been considered, however, were whether the defense, in its burden
of presenting "evidence," would have to present "sufficient evidence . . . to support a finding that the fact
exists," as the A. L. I. Model Code of Evidence, Rule
1 (2) would require, or whether "It should suffice to put
the prosecution to its proof beyond a reasonable doubt
that the defendant shows enough to justify such doubt
upon the issue." There is no indication that it was also
considered whether some courts might not go to the
other extreme and construe the section to require only
some evidence, no matter how minimal, as the District
of Columbia Court has already done. It might be worth
further thought, whether this construction is likely to
be accepted by some courts, and if so, whether it is
desired to leave the Code provision open to such possible construction.

IMPARTIAL PSYCHIATRIC EXAMINATION; HOSPITAL COMMITMENT FOR OBSERVATION

Sec. 4.05 of the Model Penal Code provides in part:

Whenever the defendant has filed a notice of intention to
rely on the defense of mental disease or defect excluding
responsibility or there is reason to doubt his fitness to proceed, or reason to believe that mental disease or defect of
the defendant will otherwise become an issue in the cause,
the Court shall appoint at least one qualified psychiatrist
. . . to examine and report upon the mental condition of the
defendant. The Court may order the defendant committed

to a hospital or other suitable facility for the purpose of the examination for a period of not exceeding sixty days or such longer period as the Court determines to be necessary for the purpose and may direct that a qualified psychiatrist retained by the defendant be permitted to witness and participate in the examination.

It may be that in actual operation, these provisions for impartial expert examination of the defendant will be the most significant part of the Model Code's provisions governing mental irresponsibility. Professor Wechsler, the reporter, has called them "the heart of this matter."[12] It has been the spectacle of the law's reliance upon the conflicting and contradictory testimony of hired partisan experts to determine the issue of mental condition that has brought the legal procedure in these cases into reproach. Providing a means by which the jury can be given a scientifically sound and unbiased presentation of the medical facts bearing on the accused's mental condition will probably be more helpful than any change in the substantive rules governing responsibility.

Court appointment of impartial experts as a method of providing such unbiased evidence is not a new proposal. At least twenty-two states and the federal rules of both civil and criminal procedure permit such appointment. It has been recommended in all the prior "model" codes and acts—the Uniform Expert Testimony Bill of 1914, the Model Code of Criminal Procedure of 1930, the Model Code of Evidence of 1942 and the Uniform Rules of Evidence of 1953.

At least eighteen states have gone further and authorized the commitment to the hospital for purposes of observation and examination which Sec. 4.05 also permits. This device has been eminently successful wherever it has been tried.[13]

One novel addition provided by the section is that permitting a psychiatrist for the defense to witness and participate in the examination. Psychiatrists have long said that if they were allowed to consult and confer together, there would probably be fewer conflicts of opinion than now appear in the court room, where the witnesses must present their opinions in answer to carefully phrased questions of the attorneys. Even the most biased expert will have some difficulty in attacking in the court room an examination in which he participated, and at which he would probably have been ashamed to raise the unsound objections which counsel may encourage on the witness stand.

One situation not clearly covered by Sec. 4.05 may arise when the prosecution or the court wishes to have the defendant's mental condition examined, but the defendant objects. If the question is as to defendant's fitness to proceed, the section clearly requires psychiatric examination. But suppose the question is as to his mental responsibility at the time of the crime charged. If the defendant has not "filed a notice of intention to rely on the defense of mental disease or defect excluding responsibility," may the court order him examined?

If the last phrase, "reason to believe that mental disease or defect of the defendant will otherwise become an issue in the cause," is intended to cover this, what is the significance of the apparently careful distinction in wording between the preceding two clauses, which seem to require the issue of responsibility to be raised by the defendant, but allow the issue of fitness to proceed to be raised by either party or by the court itself?

Even if the section be interpreted to mean that psychiatric examination is to be ordered whenever responsibility or fitness to proceed "becomes an issue," whether the issue is raised by the defense or not, the next question is whether such interpretation would be constitutional. The comments to the section dismiss this question by saying that "the constitutionality of statutes providing for a psychiatric examination of the defendant by court-appointed experts who may be summoned by the Court to testify at the trial has been uniformly sustained in recent decades."[14]

That is broadly true, but in 1954, the Oklahoma Criminal Court of Appeal held that an analogous Oklahoma act would be unconstitutional if construed to deny defendant notice and hearing before he was ordered committed to the state hospital for observation and examination.[15] And at this writing, the same issue is pending in the Alabama courts. The former Attorney General of Alabama has been charged with the murder of a candidate pledged to clean up the Phenix City scandal. The state moved to have the defendant sent to the hospital for observation. The superintendent of the state hospital had previously filed a report stating that on personal examination, there is reason to believe that the defendant was at the time of the act or is pres-

ently "insane." Under the Alabama statute, on such a
report, the trial judge is required forthwith to order
the defendant sent to the hospital for observation and
examination. The defense, however, objected to such
an order, and the presiding judge, J. Russell McElroy,
in a ruling supported by an opinion carefully analyzing
the cases, held that issuing such an order would deprive
the defendant of his liberty without due process, and,
since he had already been released on bail, would also
violate his right to bail.[16]

The basis for this viewpoint is understandable. The
order of commitment, even though it is merely for a
period of observation which will not run for more than
sixty days (under the Model Code), is nevertheless a
fairly serious interference with a person's liberty. He is
taken away from his family and his job, and subjected to
a type of confinement which may cast reflection upon
his sanity in the minds of some people. This, it is argued,
should not be permitted to be done ex parte, without
notice and an opportunity to be heard. It is not at all
certain that other courts may not take the position taken
in Oklahoma and Alabama. It would therefore seem
well to provide in the comments accompanying the
final draft of the Code a well documented brief in support of the constitutionality of this device, especially of
the provision for confinement in the hospital, which
raises more serious constitutional doubts than mere
provision for appointing impartial experts to examine
the defendant. A convincing argument for constitu-

tionality can be made.[17] But it needs to be done, to help fend off attacks.

Sec. 4.05 goes on to set forth what the psychiatric report shall include: a description of the nature of the examination; a diagnosis of the defendant's mental condition; if he suffers from a mental disease or defect, an opinion as to his capacity to understand the proceedings and assist in his own defense; and where the issue has been raised, an opinion as to the extent, if any, to which his capacity to appreciate the criminality of his conduct or to conform to the requirements of the law was impaired at the time of the act charged. This is broad enough to permit the witness to tell what he was able to learn from his examination, without being limited to the issue of responsibility or irresponsibility. This should help give the jury a fuller picture of the mental condition, although there is reason to fear that the examination and cross-examination will still tend to focus on the last part—whether he has the capacities which spell responsibility or irresponsibility. But this objection goes to the substantive test that the Code sets up, and is not a matter of procedure as such.

Similar provisions in Sec. 4.07(4) provide that any psychiatrist who has examined the defendant and who takes the stand to testify, shall be permitted to make similar broad statements as to his examination, his diagnosis, and explanations to clarify his diagnosis and his opinion.

These provisions should go far to meet complaints of psychiatrists concerning the procedural restrictions under which they are now compelled to present their findings in court—for example, questions asking for categorical "yes" or "no" answers, the limitations imposed by the question method as against exposition, the narrowness of legal focus, hypothetical questions, insufficient time in which to make adequate examinations, and failure of courts to give proper importance to the history in a medical case.

They should also go far to eliminate criticisms such as that of the Pennsylvania Supreme Court a few years ago:

> The profession and prestige of psychiatry has been gravely damaged by the testimony of some of its experts on the subject of insanity in homicide cases, as a result of which considerable doubt of the soundness or dependability of their conclusions has been raised in the minds of courts and juries alike.[18]

FITNESS TO STAND TRIAL

Sec. 4.06 deals with the procedure to be followed when the defendant's fitness to stand trial is drawn in question. It provides that this issue is to be determined "by the Court." At common law, it was within the trial court's discretion whether to decide the question itself, or to impanel a jury for the purpose. Statutes in some states today expressly reserve this discretion; thirteen other states provide for a hearing but do not specify whether the judge may impanel a jury; and in eleven states a jury trial is mandatory.[19] The Code, in excluding jury trial, thus takes what is still a minority position but one which has been growing in popularity.

As already mentioned, an impartial psychiatric examination and report is required whenever there is doubt of the defendant's fitness to proceed. If neither party contests the psychiatric report, the court may dispose of the question on that report, without taking further testimony. If there is a contest, a hearing is held. If the report is received in evidence, the party contesting the finding may summon and cross-examine the psychiatrists who joined in the report.

If found unfit to plead, the defendant is of course committed for as long as such unfitness shall last. Whether the defendant has regained fitness to proceed is to be determined by the court, after a hearing, upon application of the proper officials. This seems a leaning over backward to give the accused due process. It would seem sufficient to leave it to the hospital superintendent and his staff to make a conclusive determination of such recovery. After all, the hospital people are in a position to know better than anyone else; they have had the person in their custody. Such a determination should not be considered one which constitutionally requires court action. It is not a determination of guilt or innocence, but only of competency to stand trial. The majority of states allow the determination to be made by the hospital superintendent or by the court upon certification of the superintendent without a hearing.[20] The District of Columbia Court of Appeals has held in accordance with the Code proposal, that recovery of competency to proceed is to be found only by a judicial determination.[21] A committe of the Council on Law Enforcement of the District of Columbia has expressed the opinion that "in every instance where the accused is dissatisfied with the superintendent's certificate of recovery of competency accused should be entitled to a judicial determination, but, in the absence of objection by accused, the certificate should be sufficient to permit the court to enter an order thereon finding accused competent and directing his trial to proceed."

"The primary objection," said the committee, "to the rule requiring a judicial determination in *every* case on the question of whether or not an accused has recovered his competency is that it unnecessarily consumes a great deal of time of hospital authorities in coming into court to testify in person to matters adequately covered by their written report. In some instances hospital authorities have been required to travel long distances and to be absent from their duties for several days in order to meet this requirement."[22]

The Code wisely provides that "if, however, the Court is of the view that so much time has elapsed since the commitment of the defendant that it would be unjust to resume the criminal proceedings, the court may dismiss the charge and may order the defendant to be committed to an appropriate institution . . . or discharged." This is a recognition of the fact that unless the period of commitment for incompetency has been fairly short, it will be practically difficult and perhaps unjust for the state now to resume prosecution. Witnesses will have died or disappeared, resentment cooled or evaporated. And if at the original time for trial the accused was found to be so grossly disordered as to be incompetent to stand trial, and he has remained in that condition for a period of years thereafter, it raises sufficient doubt of his mental responsibility at the time of the act to impugn the justice of prosecuting him for that act now.

DISPOSITION OF DEFENDANT FOUND IRRESPONSIBLE ON REPORT

If the psychiatric report is to the effect that the defendant was mentally irresponsible, the court may accept the report and without more ado, enter judgment of acquittal on the ground of mental irresponsibility. Sec. 4.07. This would change existing law in that it would not allow the District Attorney in such a situation to insist upon a trial. This is a salutary provision, designed to foster and support non-contested determinations of the mental issue.

Of the other provisions concerning expert testimony, only one or two need be specifically mentioned. Sec. 4.07(3) provides that "no one who has not examined the defendant shall be competent to testify to his opinion as a psychiatrist with respect to the mental condition or responsibility of the defendant, as distinguished from the validity of the procedure followed by, or the general scientific propositions stated by, another witness." This is intended to prevent a psychiatrist who has not examined the defendant from giving an opinion

based only upon observation of him in court. Under
existing rules of evidence, such opinion is admissible.[23]

The provision is also intended to prevent such a
psychiatrist from testifying upon hypothetical questions
—although it does not seem clearly to effectuate this
purpose. In theory, a hypothetical question does not ask
about the "mental condition or responsibility of the
defendant"; it describes a *hypothetical* case—hence the
name. It is true that the hypothetical being whose
existence the witness is asked to assume will typically
bear a striking albeit distorted resemblance to the
prisoner before the court; in fact, details not proved or
hoped to be proved in the actual case should not be
included in the hypothetical question. Nevertheless, the
question is asked concerning this hypothetical person,
and not concerning the defendant. It is therefore possible that some courts may not interpret this provision
to exclude hypothetical questions, of whatever sort.
Assuming that it would be a good thing to get rid of the
hypothetical question,[24] the language should be bol-
stered to effectuate this purpose.

TRIAL OF THE INSANITY ISSUE

Although the Code requires written notice of intent
to rely on mental irresponsibility as a defense, it does
not call for a separate trial of this issue. A small number
of states (California, Colorado, Georgia and Texas) have
provided for such separation of the issues. The rationale
seems to be that it aids the orderly disposition of the

case to try the insanity issue separately (either before
other isues if any, as in Texas, or after, as in California).
Another consideration, though probably a minor one,
is that it may put the defense in a difficult position to
have to argue in the same proceeding, first, that the
accused did not commit the crime, and second, that if he
did, he was mentally irresponsible at the time.

But the cases where both defenses are seriously advanced are probably rare. Where the defense is insanity the commission of the act charged is usually
clearly established and perhaps conceded. Even where
both lines of defense are actually litigated, it is probably
true as Sir Norwood East has said that "as the case pro-
ceeds the jury get their minds fixed on certain points
and a certain atmosphere develops round the jury box
and in the whole Court which is important . . . and that
atmosphere will probably drift away, rightly or wrongly,
by the time the trial is taken on a later day."[25]

But the fatal blow to the separate trial device has been
struck by the rise of the rule that mental disorder, even
if not so serious as to come within the test of mental
irresponsibility, may still be proved and must still be
taken into account in determining whether the defendant had the specific intent. Thus if the charge is
first degree murder, and if making out that charge requires proof of a deliberate and premeditated homicide,
proof that the defendant did not in fact deliberate and
premeditate the killing—either because he was mentally
incapable of such deliberating and premeditating, or

because of any other reason—forbids his being found
guilty of first degree murder. Not all state courts have
accepted this reasoning,[26] but California and Colorado
are among those who have. And the courts of both these
states have held that evidence of mental condition introduced for this purpose may be introduced in the trial
of the main issue of guilt or innocence.[27] This is probably sound in theory, but it wholly defeats the purpose
of the separate trial device. The testimony concerning
mental condition, instead of being separated, is largely
duplicated. Complete duplication can be avoided only
by drawing an artificial line between evidence going
only to prove lack of specific intent and evidence tending to prove irresponsibility. Trying to maintain this
line forces the court to indulge in judicial hairsplitting,
creates confusion and uncertainty while the bar awaits
the results of such hairsplitting, and encourages appeals
on alleged errors in the hairsplitting process. For evidence, the reader is referred to the heroic efforts of the
California courts during the past twenty-eight years to
fight their way out of this quagmire.[28] The Code draftsmen were wise not to encourage additional states to
walk into it.

DISPOSITION OF DEFENDANT ACQUITTED
ON GROUND OF MENTAL IRRESPONSIBILITY

Section 4.08 provides that when a defendant is acquitted on the groud of mental disease or defect excluding responsibility, the court "shall" order him committed

into custody to be placed in a proper institution for custody, care and treatment.

This differs from the legislation in most states mainly in that it is mandatory. Most states provide that on such a verdict the court *"may"* order him committed. In most cases, both wordings will work the same way, for even under the permissive wording a judge will rarely if ever consider it proper to do anything other than order commitment for a defendant so acquitted. The insanity issue is usually raised only in cases of murder or other serious charges. A person who has just convinced a court that at the time of the act he was so seriously disordered as to have been criminally irresponsible has himself proved adequate grounds to justify his commitment until there is some assurance that he is no longer dangerous.

On the other hand, a model code should be tailored to fit the possible future as well as the present. Advances in psychiatry make it quite possible that in the near future a person who at the time of the act was irresponsible, may by the time of the trial have been wholly cured—by some new drug or new surgical operation, for example. It may be said that even though such cases may be rare, the judge should have discretion to make other provision, such as probation or even full discharge, where that is justified. To this, it may be answered that it is not unreasonable to require commitment even in such cases. The judge is not the best person to determine whether there has been full recovery and no danger of

relapse exists. That can be better decided by the hospital authorities after a period of observation.

A second question, not answered by the Code provisions, is whether the jury is to be informed of what
will be done with the defendant if he is acquitted by
reason of mental irresponsibility. In most states, the
jury is not so informed. The theory is that that is a
matter for the judge and is no concern of the jury.[29]
But the fact is that jurors *do* concern themselves with it.
Preliminary statistics on the Jury Project being conducted by the University of Chicago Law School show
that this is indeed one of the most important factors in
the jury deliberations. "If we acquit him on the ground
of insanity," the jury wants to know, "will he be set at
liberty to repeat his act?" Not a single jury studied in
the Jury Project refrained from considering what would
happen to the defendant as a precondition for arriving
at a decision concerning his guilt or innocence, sanity or
insanity. In almost every instance the basic issue around
which the discussion centered was what would happen
to him if they decided in a particular manner. During
the deliberations, many jurors who were somewhat disposed toward a verdict of insanity were brought over
to a guilty verdict by the argument that if declared
insane the defendant would go "scot free." They were
won over because the court had not instructed them on
what actually would happen on such a verdict.

Since juries apparently are going to concern themselves about the disposition of the defendant if he is
found insane, it would be better if they were given the

correct answer instead of being allowed to act on mis-information and misapprehensions. It would therefore be well if other courts adopted the view recently accepted by the Court of Appeals for the District of Columbia, that where the defendant pleads insanity, counsel may and the judge should inform the jury what disposition will be made of him if he is acquitted by reason of insanity. Though this fact has no theoretical bearing on the jury's verdict, it may as the court said have a practical bearing.[30]

Such a ruling is not foreclosed under the Model Penal Code, which is merely silent on the point. But since the prevailing rule seems to be otherwise, it might be well to include an express provision.

RELEASE ON RECOVERY

A person committed upon being acquitted of crime by reason of mental irresponsibility is not to be released until this may be done "without danger to himself or to others." Sec. 4.08 (2). This phrasing is an improvement over the more usual provisions now found in most states, which either provide merely that the defendant so acquitted shall be committed until restored to sanity or until he becomes sane, or apply the civil commitment criterion for release.

Although it was suggested above that a judicial hearing to determine whether a person committed as unfit to stand trial has not sufficiently recovered to be tried is perhaps unnecessary in every case, it is proper and usual to provide that a person acquitted of crime because he was mentally irresponsible at the time of the act should be committed to a mental hospital and not released except upon court order. The Code procedure for determining the question seems well suited both to protect the individual against arbitrary and unduly prolonged restraint and to protect the public against release while he is still dangerous. If the hospital authorities report to the court that the person may be discharged or released on probation without danger to himself or others, the court is to appoint two psychiatrists to make an examination and report. If the court is satisfied from the report (and the testimony of the psychiatrists making the report if the court wishes to hear their testimony) that the person may safely be released, it may order discharge or release on probation. If not so satisfied, the court shall order a hearing.

The committed person may himself make application for discharge as recovered, but no such application need be considered until he has been confined for at least six months, and if the application be denied, further application may be filed only at one year intervals. This restriction on the frequency of application reflects sound policy.

The public can probably be protected better by making sure that those so acquitted will not promptly be released, than by a strict "test" of mental irresponsibility. In the discussion at the 1955 meeting of the American Law Institute, there was mentioned an Oregon case, in which the state hospital doctor testified that in his opinion the girl who had killed her lover had done so because he had jilted her for another, and that she was not insane. The jury found her insane, and sent her to the hospital. The doctor stood by his judgment and promptly released her as sane. Under the Code, this could not happen. It might be illogical that the law should insist on keeping a person in the hospital as insane, when the hospital people, who probably know best what his condition is, say he is sane. But it is one way of making sure that defendants cannot play fast and loose with the law. If they succeed in convincing a jury that they are insane, they are going to be confined as insane at least for a certain length of time.

It has been urged that all persons released on recovery after confinement on an acquittal by reason of insanity should be subject to some kind of psychiatric aftercare supervision for a period of time.[31] But only a few states make any provision for conditional release. The Code's provision for release on probation is a step in the right direction. To make this fully effective, however, the state will have to provide facilities for supervising the person on such probation—psychiatric probation officers.

PRIVILEGED COMMUNICATIONS

In jurisdictions where statutes make communications between doctor and patient privileged (which includes all but some seventeen states), the provision for hospital observation and report by court appointed experts may give rise to this question: may a defendant who has been

so observed or examined upon court order object to the
doctors' testifying as to his condition, on the ground
that the information they acquired is privileged?

The Court of Appeals for the District of Columbia
has answered this question in the affirmative.[32] One
Taylor had been found incompetent to stand trial when
he was first arraigned, and had therefore been committed. Seven months later, the hospital reported him
competent, and he was brought to trial. To rebut his
contention that he was mentally irresponsible at the
time of the crime, the prosecution offered the attending
physician in the hospital ward where Taylor had been
confined, who had regularly observed and treated him
during his stay there. He testified that Taylor was sane,
and also that Taylor had admitted he was not suffering
from delusions and hallucinations as he had claimed,
but was merely "going along with a gag" in describing
such episodes.

The Court of Appeals held that the trial court had
erred in permitting the doctor to so testify, because the
testimony violated the statutory physician-patient privilege. The court pointed out that the doctor had not
merely observed, but had treated the defendant. The
court conceded that the privilege does not apply where
the doctor merely observes or examines the person, as
where he does so for the prosecution in order to qualify
himself for testifying as a witness in the trial. But where
the accused is committed to a hospital for a more or
less indeterminate period, as in this case, where commitment was until he becomes sane enough to stand

trial, most hospitals would consider it their function not merely to observe, but also to treat, and to try to facilitate recovery. Under the Taylor case reasoning, the privilege statute would prevent any staff doctor from testifying in such case. This would to a large extent defeat the purpose of the statute providing for hospitalization for observation and report.

The Model Code undertakes to meet this situation by providing that "A statement made by a person subjected to psychiatric examination or treatment pursuant to Sections 4.05, 4.06 or 4.08 for the purpose of such examination or treatment shall not be admissible in evidence against him in any criminal proceeding on any issue other than that of his mental condition but it shall be admissible upon that issue, whether or not it would otherwise be deemed to be a privileged communication."

This specifically extends to "treatment." On the other hand, it limits admissibility of the doctor's testimony to the issue of mental condition, and does not go so far as to allow the doctor to relate statements of the patient tending to prove guilt, for example. Moreover, the privilege is limited to criminal proceedings; it does not extend, for example, to actions for appointment of a guardian.

The Code provision seems sound, even from the viewpoint of those of us who favor retention of the privilege in psychiatric cases.[33] That the privilege may be useful in ordinary psychiatrist-patient relationships does not necessarily require that it be extended to these cases of hospitalization on court order. The reason for the privilege is to encourage people to seek psychiatric care and treatment when they need it. To get any help from consulting a psychiatrist, the patient must be willing to bare his most shameful and most secret deeds and thoughts, including deeds which might subject him to criminal conviction if the psychiatrist could be compelled to reveal them on the witness stand. To promote the policy of encouraging people to seek psychiatric help when they need it, it is worth while sacrificing what little help law enforcement might get from being able to force such revelations from the suspect's psychiatrist.

But this consideration is minor or negligible when the person is in a hospital by court order, in order that his mental condition may be determined for purposes of criminal proceedings. This is not a situation where we need to encourage the patient voluntarily to consult a psychiatrist by promising him silence. He is being sent to the psychiatrist by court order. Silence cannot save him from criminal proceedings or from more disgrace than he already faces. He is already charged with crime. What he reveals to the court-appointed psychiatrist is not likely to reveal facts that will place him in a worse light than if he remains silent, and it may help him to avoid the stigma of "guilt" by revealing mental disorder.

Pre-Sentence Investigation

We are not always aware how radically the sentencing function of the judge has been changed by substituting the ideal of rehabilitative treatment for the old ideal of retribution. So long as our object was to make the punishment fit the crime, it was reasonable to fix the punishment by statute, or to fix maxima and minima and leave it to the judge to set the term within those limits. Discriminatory differences resulted, when one judge imposed a minimum sentence and another judge the maximum for cases which seemed very much alike.[34] This was a serious defect in even-handed application, but it did not invalidate the principle of trying to set a "just" punishment.

But now that we have, at least in theory, moved to the position that wrongdoers should be rehabilitated rather than merely made to suffer for their sins, it is expecting much too much to hope that the judge will be able to fix even a roughly approximate time within which the convicted criminal can be reformed, if at all, merely upon hearing the evidence concerning the commission of a single offense, divorced from all the (legally) irrelevant facts of his life history, including prior behavior. As Harry Elmer Barnes has said, "to set definite time sentences—even maximum and minimum—is as preposterous as it would be for a judge, in a mental case, to sentence a patient to a mental hospital for ten years for dementia praecox, to fifteen years for involutional melancholia, and to twenty years for paranoia."[35]

Criminologists and psychiatrists tend to favor a system in which the judge's function would be to conduct the trial to determine whether the defendant did in fact

commit the act charged. The problem of what to do
with the accused if it is found that he did commit the
act would be turned over to a tribunal of experts qualified to evaluate psychiatric, psychological and sociological data.[36] But this is not likely to happen in the
foreseeable future, even if it could be done without
encountering constitutional obstacles.[37] Perhaps even
from a psychological viewpoint it is well to keep the
sentencing function in the judge. "The symbol of the
wise and just father, punishing wrongdoers, probably
adds to the stability of society and to the average individual's feeling of security."[38]

But if the judge is to retain the sentencing function,
we should enable him, through pre-sentence investigation, to obtain some information about the defendant's
personality and his socio-cultural background, and especially about those subsurface emotional conflicts of
which the criminal act is so often only one—perhaps
almost accidental—manifestation or symptom. Such
investigation may aid the state as well as the defendant
by providing a check on the trial process and keeping
disordered or defective persons from being sent to penal
institutions, where they would be a source of disciplinary difficulty.

The Model Penal Code in Sec. 7.07 requires a pre-
sentence investigation in certain cases and permits it in
any case. It adds:

Before imposing sentence, the Court may order the defendant to submit to psychiatric observation and examination for a period of not exceeding sixty days or such longer

period as the Court determines to be necessary for the purpose. The defendant may be remanded for this purpose to any available clinic or mental hospital or the Court may appoint a qualified psychiatrist to make the examination. The report of the examination shall be submitted to the Court.

Psychiatry can make a valuable contribution at this point in the proceedings, as new legislation in a number of states is recognizing.[39] As long ago as 1929 the American Bar Association recommended that "no criminal be sentenced for any felony . . . until there be filed as a part of the record a psychiatric report."[40] In 1950, the International Penal and Penitentiary Commission Congress unanimously endorsed pre-sentence examination.[41]

CONCLUSION

The work of drafting the Model Penal Code is far from finished. What has been drafted is still in tentative form. But the sections discussed above, dealing with the procedure for handling the issue of mental responsibility and competency to stand trial, are fairly complete and provide carefully designed machinery for determining these issues. In so far as improvement in legal procedure can facilitate disposition of these cases, the Code offers what is indeed a model which the Institute can with pride submit for adoption by the states.

CHAPTER SIX

The Urge to Punish

Most of the criticisms of the law governing mental disorder as a defense in criminal law mentioned in this book have been repeated for decades. Why then has so little been done about them?

Here, as is true of other defects and shortcomings in our criminal law principles and practices, inaction has probably been due not so much to logical rejection of proposed reforms as to irrational preconceptions and prejudices.

It is not only criminals who are motivated by irrational and emotional impulsions. The same is true also of lawyers and judges, butchers and bakers. And it is especially true on such a subject as punishment of criminals. This is a matter on which we are all inclined to have deep feelings. When a reprehensible crime is committed, strong emotional reactions take place in all of us. Some people will be impelled to go out at once and work off their tensions in a lynching orgy. Even the calmest, most law-abiding of us is likely to be deeply stirred. All our ingrained concepts of morality and "justice" come into play, all our ancient tribal fears of anything that threatens the security of the group. It is one of the marks of a civilized culture that it has devised legal procedures that minimize the impact of emotional reactions and strive for calm and rational disposition. But lawyers, judges and jurors are still human, and objective, rational inquiry is made difficult by the very irrationality of the human mind itself.

Many of the judicial explanations for refusing to relax the traditional tests are so obviously baseless that they can only be taken as emotional reactions rather than as reasons. How else can one explain judicial pronouncements that liberalizing the right-and-wrong test would be dangerous to society, would render prosecution for crime impossible, and in effect would break down the fabric of civilization?[1]

This problem, of course, is not peculiar to our field. All social science suffers from it. All social science research is likely to have its data colored and its propositions distorted by fear and by prejudice, for religious dogma, ethical concepts, social outlook and economic interests are likely to be deeply involved. These may have more unconscious than conscious impact, and the unconscious is the more dangerous. Consciously we want to be rational. We prefer to think of ourselves as governed by reason rather than as creatures swept by irrational emotions or sluggishly adhering to the old rules because they protect us against the painful sensation of doubt and the still more painful task of rethinking and re-examining old solutions.

Socrates' admonition, "know thyself," calls for emotional maturity and psychological insight. We need more of both before we fully understand why we treat criminals as we do, and why we hold so desperately to the M'Naghten rule.

It is only in recent times that we have dared to suspect that even judicial opinion may be subject to this tendency to rationalize, to suggest that the reasons judges set forth for their conclusions may not actually be the premises which led to the conclusion, but that the conclusion may have come first, as a non-rational emotional reaction, or as an unarticulated "hunch," with the reasons being contrived afterward to bolster the decision already reached. This subjecting of the judicial process to psychological scrutiny is no reflection on the bench. It is rather a sign of growing cultural maturity that we are willing to recognize the existence of irrational processes, because only if we honestly face the fact of their existence can we hope to limit their effects.

Let us take a look at some of the arguments that have been advanced for refusing to relax the traditional tests of insanity, and in particular, for refusing to accept the New Hampshire Durham case rule. I have already discussed such arguments as that the traditional test is clear and certain whereas the new proposal is allegedly too loose and uncertain, and the converse argument that the traditional test is so flexible that it can be stretched to cover every proper case. Here I want to consider some other arguments, arguments that rest on a psychological attitude, the all-too-human urge to punish. The arguments take various forms.

It is argued that the new test would, because of its liberality or its looseness, result in the release of numerous dangerous criminals against whom the public should be protected, that it would encourage malingering, and that it would flout the public demand for retributive "justice." When the Durham case was decided, the United States Attorney for the District of Columbia was reported as fearing "that the new rule will greatly increase the number of insanity pleas in criminal cases, multiply the work of psychiatrists, bog down prosecutions and bring about the release of criminals from whom the public should be protected."[2]

More than a year has now passed since the Durham decision. I recently inquired how the rule was working. The chairman of the committee on mental disorder as a criminal defense of the Council on Law Enforcement of the District of Columbia replied:

I think it is safe to say that the fears expressed at the time the Durham decision was announced, to the effect that the number of insanity pleas in criminal cases would be greatly increased, have not materialized. I have kept in rather constant contact with the local United States Attorney's office in connection with this matter, and I am sure that they now feel that their original fears were unfounded.

I think it also safe to say that the fears at first entertained that more criminals would be acquitted on the ground of insanity have likewise not materialized. The findings of "not guilty by reason of insanity" do not certainly appear to have increased and I think it is more than possible that the number, percentagewise, has decreased.[3]

The only other jurisdiction that has accepted this rule, New Hampshire, certainly has not been plagued with an undue number of insanity pleas. There are few statistics, but I have made as careful an inquiry as I could about the operation of the law in that state. Judge Amos N. Blandin, Jr. of the New Hampshire Supreme Court canvassed the judges and prosecuting attorneys of the state for me, and Professor Arthur E. Prell, sociologist of the University of New Hampshire, canvassed the psychiatrists and sociologists. There seems to be complete satisfaction with the operation of the rule on the part of all concerned. I do not pretend that this was a scientifically valid study. New Hampshire is too small, too free from crime—unfortunately for research purposes—and also too free from statistical records, to permit statistically valid conclusions. But it certainly can be said that the available evidence does not in the least support the idea that the New Hampshire rule has resulted in undue pleas of insanity. No criminal case involving the rule governing mental irresponsibility has been appealed to the state Supreme Court since 1871. In no other state have there been so few cases.

As for releasing too many dangerous persons into the community, we must remember that a person acquitted of crime by reason of insanity is not released; he is sent to a mental hospital. And the statistics show that persons so committed are kept confined *longer* than they would have been if they had been convicted of the crime charged.[4] It is true that if the new rule is construed to include psychopaths, we may find cases where a psychopath is acquitted because of his disorder, sent to a mental hospital, and shortly thereafter released because he is not psychotic. But the way to meet this problem is not by keeping a narrow general test of irresponsibility. Instead, it should be met by providing that persons so committed should not be released until they are *no longer dangerous,* or, better yet, by legislation dealing directly with the problem of the psychopaths.

As for malingering, the short answer is that the medical problem of detecting malingerers has practically nothing to do with the legal test of irresponsibility. That problem will be no more and no less difficult under the Durham case rule than under the right-and-wrong or any other. Dr. Ray said long ago, that, "The supposed insurmountable difficulty of distinguishing between feigned and real insanity has conduced, probably more than all other causes together, to bind the legal profession to the most rigid construction and application of the common law relative to this disease, and is always put forward in objection to the more humane doctrines that have been inculcated in the present work."[5]

Even in 1838, Dr. Ray was able to devote a whole chapter, of thirty pages, in his *Medical Jurisprudence* to explaining how simulated insanity might be distinguished from the genuine. Most of what he said is still quite sound, and a lot of knowledge has been added since. Yet probably the majority of judges today are almost as ignorant of these means for distinguishing as

they were then. Most judges who fear that liberalizing
the test would facilitate malingering would be reassured
by reading that chapter. For further assurance, they
might read about newer discoveries that psychoanalysis
and other techniques have added, as well as new mechanical methods such as the EEG and the lie detector,
truth serums, etc. Dr. Henry Davidson's short chapter
on the subject, in his *Forensic Psychiatry,* should dispose of any exaggerated fears on this score.

More basic is the argument that the "instinctive sense
of justice" of the community will be offended if we
adopt a rule that fails to mete out punishment where
punishment seems to the public to be deserved. As Dr.
Franz Alexander has argued, when a defendant escapes
who, people think, deserves punishment, they may lose
faith in the social structure and may relax their own
inhibitions.[6] "If he escapes his just deserts," they may
tend to think, "why should I continue to obey the law?"
The public is willing to recognize the mentally irresponsible as a class that should be exempted from punishment, since it is futile to threaten and punish people
who cannot be "cured or taught a lesson" by such
sanctions. But the exception must be narrowly restricted.
Professor Herbert Wechsler has well stated this argument: "The category must be so extreme that to the
ordinary man, burdened by passion and beset by large
temptations, the exculpation of the irresponsible be-
speaks no weakness in the law. He does not identify
himself and them: they are a world apart. . . . Beyond
such extreme incapacities however, the exception can-

not go. This, to be sure, is not poetic justice. It is public justice, which in the interest of the common good prescribes a standard all must subscribe to who can, those whose nature or nurture leads them to conform with difficulty no less than those who find compliance easy."[7]

Eminent jurists have told us that we must be careful to heed and respect this public demand for punitive "justice." Public "qualms at the prospect of a softening of retribution," we are told, "deserve attention, and should, so far as is compatible with advance rather than regression in the penal field, be relieved."[8] "The first requirement of a sound body of law," said Mr. Justice Holmes, "is that it should correspond with the actual feelings and demands of the community, whether right or wrong."[9] Perhaps the strongest such statement is the famous remark of Sir James Stephen, who said: "I think it highly desirable that criminals should be hated, that the punishment inflicted on them should be so contrived as to give expression to that hatred, and to justify it so far as the public provision of means for expressing and gratifying a healthy natural sentiment can justify and encourage it."[10]

But let us take a look at this "instinctive sense of justice" the public is supposed to feel so keenly, and that we are so anxious to mollify. "Justice" is a noble word, and the use of it implies we have here a noble sentiment.

But psychiatrists have been holding up the mirror to

this sentiment, and the picture they see is not so pretty. The urge to punish wrongdoers is not always an impersonal demand that the law keep its promises. Often it is an outlet for our own antisocial aggressiveness which we have more or less effectively but guiltily repressed. "It is a weapon in our own struggle against trends and drives which we do not admit to consciousness. We should be continuously aware that over-assertion of a prosecuting, punishing, attitude toward law breakers reveals the intensity of our inner struggle and the instability of our own emotional equilibrium."[11] "Distrust," said Nietzsche, "all in whom the impulse to punish is strong." No one is more ferocious in demanding that the murderer or the rapist "pay" for his crime than the man who has felt strong impulses in the same direction. No one is more bitter in condemning the "loose" woman than the "good" women who have on occasion guiltily enjoyed some purple dreams themselves. It is never he who is without sin who casts the first stone.

Along with the stone, we cast our own sins onto the criminal. In this way we relieve our own sense of guilt without actually having to suffer the punishment—a convenient and even pleasant device for it not only relieves us of sin, but makes us feel actually virtuous. A criminal trial, like a prize fight, is a public performance in which the spectators work off in a socially acceptable way aggressive impulses of much the same kind that the man on trial worked off in a socially unacceptable way.

We even piously quote Scripture to justify our vindictiveness: "An eye for an eye and a tooth for a tooth." But what that says, as the Archbishop of Canterbury pointed out, was that one must not exact *more* than an eye for an eye. "It was not an exhortation that you should exact an equivalent, but it said that if somebody knocked your tooth out, morality requires that you do no more than knock one of his out. It is a restraint on the passions of mankind . . . no Christian law says you must exact equivalent penalty. Indeed, Christianity works on the other principle, that whatever the crime, you should seek to remedy it by the operation of redemption and love."[12]

The phenomenon is perhaps analagous to Aldous Huxley's theory of why war was more popular in the days when it was less dangerous to civilians. Those back home identified with their armies, and shared in their glories.[13] So today the individual who reads about an atrocious crime in the newspaper identifies with society, makes the crime a personal affront to himself, and demands strong-arm retaliation.

This strong but largely unconscious impulse to punish in others the tendencies that we deny or repress in ourselves may provide a partial explanation for the hostility that psychiatrists sometimes feel to their testimony. "A peculiar feature of psychiatric evidence is that it is directed not to the external facts of the case but to facts relevant to the accused's moral responsibility, and it is therefore in its very nature apt to create an emotional disturbance in the minds of the jury."[14] Especially in cases of violent or sexual crimes, the emotionally disturbing conflict between feelings of guilty identification and of righteous indignation will be strong. The result is likely to be powerful feelings of criticism and hostility against those who present such disturbing evidence.

As for Stephen's notion that hatred of criminals is a "healthy natural sentiment" that should be encouraged, we may concede that it is natural, human nature being something less than Christlike, but modern psychology would hardly call it healthy. Hatred is not health. It is a poison. It will cripple and even kill the individual or the society that feeds on it. The function of law is to hold the brute forces of hate and vindictiveness in check—not to encourage them. The history of law is the story of the slow—painfully slow—steps by which society, one short step at a time, restricted this and that manifestation of these forces. They yielded each step only slowly and after long and stubborn opposition. If we open the door to them, it will be hard to close again. The Nazi regime was an outstandingly terrible example of the dangers that engulf a society where official sanction is given to the brute forces of hatred.

The primitive and irrational nature of the urge to punish is demonstrated by the fact that it is murder and sex crimes that bring our blood to the boiling point. But the real threat to social well being and security in our society does not arise out of these anachronistic and atavistic acts of a few abnormal individuals. Our real crime problem is the white collar crime and organized racketeering that costs us annually at least ten times as much as all the old-fashioned crimes of violence put together. And before anyone charges me with equating mere money losses with crimes against life and person, let me say that there is a personal tragedy also when a small businessman is hounded to bankruptcy and suicide by racketeers. It is merely primitive impulse that causes us to bay for the blood of murderers and rapists, but accept with philosophic equanimity the existence of thousands of racketeers, swindlers, fraudulent promoters and clever operators in high places, who cost the nation billions in losses every year.

The danger is that the irrational urge to do something emotionally satisfying will brush aside calmer efforts to do something constructive. "Aggressiveness, a heritage from the past based on fear, ignorance, and frustration, is becoming an increasingly heavy burden for civilized man to bear. How to substitute for it co-operation and harmonious interpersonal relationships is a problem which increasing knowledge of mental health may help to solve. I need not emphasize how urgent it has become to prevent 'the old savage in the new civilization' from wrecking our plans for building up a peaceful world society."[15]

And it seems to me an abdication of the leadership that the public has a right to expect of the legal profession abjectly to accept this primitive aggressiveness as inevitable and unchangeable.

It is of course a difficult question how far law can outrun public sentiment. The Negro problem is an illustration of how hard it is to change deep-rooted social customs and habits by legal fiat. For decades, the Supreme Court dodged the responsibility of making the Civil War amendments really effective and compel the southern states to give Negroes political equality. The court apparently agreed with Carter, that "the attempt to compel a community of men to do right by legislative command, when they do not think it to be right, is tyranny."[16] Charles Warren agreed that the court couldn't have done more with a problem so packed with emotional and sectional dynamite.[17]

But others thought that the court failed to seize an opportunity to exert a great moral and educative influence. And in recent years, the court has shown a greater willingness to exert leadership, with results still to be seen. The court has been confronted with the same problem of choice between following and leading public opinion in the field of civil liberties. The difference in viewpoints is brought into high relief in two recent little books. One is *The Supreme Court in the American System of Government,* by the late Mr. Justice Robert H. Jackson; the other is *National Security and Individual Freedom,* by John Lord O'Brian. Mr. Justice Jackson had been selected to deliver the Godkin lectures at Harvard University. He prepared the lectures but died before he could deliver them. His book contains these undelivered lectures. On his death, John Lord O'Brian was asked to step into the breach, and his book contains the lectures that he did deliver. On this matter of leadership versus followership the two reveal an interesting and important difference in emphasis. Jackson's emphasis is on what the court cannot do. "Any court," he wrote, "which undertakes by its legal processes to enforce civil liberties needs the support of an enlightened and vigorous public opinion. . . . I do not think the American public is enlightened on this subject."

O'Brian on the other hand takes the view that the public needs and should be provided leadership toward understanding, instead of being merely passively followed, and he deplores the "scarcity of leaders courageous and outspoken in the cause of individual freedom."

There is of course essential truth in both positions, but I stand with O'Brian in feeling that the emphasis belongs on the need for leadership, in civil liberties and in penal philosophy. The human thirst for vengeance, the human instincts of hate and fear, need no encouragement from the law. So long as they exist, we must of course take them into account, but we need not reinforce them and give them dignity by legal endorsement.

I even venture to guess that the public thirst for vengeance is not as great as courts have seemed to fear. Law and order will not collapse if we frankly repudiate blind vengeance. Public opinion today is different from what it was in Stephen's day—and the dominant opinion was probably not as blood-thirsty in Stephen's day as his statement assumed. For the past two or three centuries, public opinion has generally been less retributive than the law itself. It was public opinion that forced the law to become more humanitarian. In the eighteenth century, juries simply refused to follow the law that called for capital punishment for grand larceny. They either acquitted, or found defendants guilty of stealing goods of the value of 39 shillings (40 shillings made it capital)—regardless of the value of the goods they were proved to have stolen or that they confessed to stealing. It was juries who ended witchcraft prosecutions, and who caused the bankers to plead for abolition of the death penalty for forgery. Not only juries, but witnesses and even victims refused to co-operate.

Today, I believe public opinion is still in advance of the law. Increased impersonality in our civilization has been added to other factors feeding this trend. From reading our criminal codes, one would get the impression that death is the standard punishment for first degree murder. In fact, the death penalty is extremely rare. Juries simply will not impose it in most cases. If death is the mandatory punishment they will not convict of that degree. That is why state after state has had to give up the mandatory death penalty.

If the legal profession is not to take the lead in the movement toward a less bloody and vengeful law, it should at least not stand in the way. If judges and lawyers cannot or will not speak up for the side of reason and understanding, it is at least time that they stop talking like apologists for the forces of hate and fear.

Understanding and love instead of hate are enjoined upon us not only by the teachings of religion but also by the teachings of psychology. We can put to death only creatures whom hatred and fear have convinced us are inhuman monsters. In war, we whip ourselves up a conviction—for the duration—that every man, woman and child in the enemy nation is a japrat, a hun, a beast. Only so can we rain bombs upon them, and live with ourselves. We could not do so to human beings like ourselves.

The injunction that we love those who hate us, that we return good for evil, is not easy to obey—as two thousand years of professed Christianity have shown. Criminals and psychopaths are likely to be unlovely and unloveable personalities. It takes profound understanding not to become discouraged and even angry with the delinquent who responds to your efforts at kindness by acting *worse* than ever. Yet this is often the most promising case. This negative response may signal a transitory phase, in which he is testing you out, to see whether your gestures of kindness are genuine, or—what his whole past life has led him to expect—insincere, phony, and probably with an ulterior "angle." With understanding and with infinite patience, this hostile attitude can be overcome. This is the kind of work that probation officers and other social workers are doing day in and day out. It is infinitely more constructive, for the person and for society, than all the impregnable prisons, and all the gallows, the electric chairs and the gas chambers in the world.

I do not mean to suggest that irrational and emotional reactions are the only motivations behind criminal punishment and that there are no rational arguments for punishment. Punishment calmly devised and admin-

istered without hate probably performs a needed function. The psychiatrist would say that by developing a
superego leading to displacement and sublimation of
elemental impulses, punishment is an important factor
in personality development and in the progress of civilization. What I do say is that the rational arguments are
not the only reasons for what we do to criminals; the
irrational elements play a much bigger role than we
admit or perhaps even consciously realize. And if we
will come to understand the motivations that lie behind
the way human beings behave—wrongdoer and righteous
both—we shall be increasingly able to supplant an emotionally charged, moralizing approach to the problem of
crime with a more scientific emphasis on social dangerousness, deterrability and treatability.

I wish to ask you to consider with me in particular the
punishment of death. The question of whether the defendant was "insane" at the time of the crime would
lose much of its consequence if we would take a step
that I believe we ought to take for a lot of additional
reasons. That is to abolish the death penalty.

The insanity defense is almost never raised except in
murder cases. A defendant charged with anything less
than a capital offense usually prefers to take his chances
on receiving a prison sentence, which will run for only
a limited number of years, rather than enter an insanity plea, which if successful will get him committed
to a mental institution indefinitely. At least the doubt-
ful cases and the cases of outright malingering would

pretty certainly be reduced if the only difference between acquittal by reason of insanity and conviction
were commitment to a mental hospital, instead of a
prison—or not even that, in states where persons so
acquitted are nevertheless sent to the *prison,* but confined in a psychiatric ward.

Absent the death penalty, if by mistake a defendant
who was actually irresponsible were found guilty, the
only practical effect would be that he'd be sent to the
prison instead of the hospital. And life in a modern
prison is not so incomparably worse than in a mental
institution that that would be a shocking injustice—
especially since after he got to the prison, if he were
found to be disordered, he could be transferred to the
hospital. On expiration of his sentence, if still not safe to
be released, he could be detained on civil commitment.

Of course, he would suffer the stigma of criminal
"guilt," instead of being acquitted on the ground of
insanity. But that is a distinction that looms larger in
the minds of moral philosophers than it probably does
for the general run of defendants. When "Three Finger"
Jack McGurk is indicted for an offense for which he
fears he might burn, his main concern is to avoid that
melancholy end. If there seems to be no other way to
avoid it, he may plead insanity. But if the death penalty
were abolished, he probably wouldn't: he'd prefer to be
found guilty and given a fixed sentence rather than seek
a commitment to a mental hospital which might last
for life. Of course the prison sentence might be for life
too. But prison life holds fewer unknown terrors than

life in an "insane asylum." Nor are those terrors all imaginary. At the hospital he may find himself strapped to a table and subjected to the painful and terrifying convulsions of electric shock or insulin shock therapy. In some states he may be sterilized. If the hospital after commitment makes a really comprehensive "criminal investigation of his unconscious," laying naked his entire personality, stripping his act of any possible glamor and perhaps even of rationality, the experience will be uncomfortable. Until he can be taught to appreciate this approach, the average criminal will prefer the prison routine, which a smart crook can live with without any disturbance to his personality—which is to say without any reform of his personality.

It is time we Americans realized that we have probably the most ferocious penal policy in the whole civilized world. Most other civilized countries have not only abolished the death penalty, but have also reduced prison sentences far below the terms we hand out here.[18] Some 36 jurisdictions throughout the world have abolished the death penalty entirely, in Europe, in South America, in Asia. Of all of the democracies of Western Europe, only England* and France retain it, and England has been seriously debating abolition. Holland has not executed any criminals since 1860, Belgium since 1863, Norway, 1875, and Denmark, 1892. In some of those countries, the death penalty is still on the statute

---

* Since this chapter was written the House of Commons on February 16, 1956, adopted a resolution looking to the prompt abolition of capital punishment.

books, but it is never used. Soviet Russia has restricted the death penalty largely if not wholly to offenders regarded as serious enemies of the state, a concept analogous to treason, though considerably broader.

In South America, the eight countries that comprise 80 percent or more of the population and of the land area of that continent have abolished capital punishment as a civil sanction. Cuba, Puerto Rico, Costa Rica and most of Mexico have done the same. In this country, six states have no death penalty.[19]

And the experience of these jurisdictions gives no evidence that abolition leads to more crime. Of the eight states having the lowest murder rate in the United States, five have no death penalty. The state with the very lowest murder rate is Maine, which abolished capital punishment in 1870. The state with the highest murder rate is Georgia. It is also the state that itself does more killing than any other, with 280 executions in twenty years as against 270 for the four times more populous New York, and 124 for the three times more populous state of Pennsylvania.[20]

If the death penalty is a deterrent, its greatest effect should be shown through executions that are well publicized. Some years ago, a study was made under the supervision of Professor Thorsten Sellin of the University of Pennsylvania, of the preventive value of such executions. Five executions were found which had received great notoriety, and which had occurred over a period of five years. On the assumption that deterrence should manifest itself by a decline or at least a temporary drop in homicides, tables were prepared showing the number of homicides committed during the sixty-day period immediately following each of these executions, as compared with the sixty-day period immediately preceding. It was found that "there were a total of 105 days *free from homicides* during the sixty-day periods before the executions and 74 in the periods after the executions. There were a total of ninety-one homicides in the 'before execution' periods and 113 in the 'after' periods."[21]

From all the statistical studies that have been made, "it seems clear that the presence or absence of the death penalty makes no particular difference in the amount of murder in a given state. Its murder rate will be closely parallel to that of adjoining states, where conditions of life and social-cultural attitudes are similar."[22] Murder is a complex sociological phenomenon, and is not controllable by simply imposing severe punishment. This is so true that students of the problems of homicide rarely discuss the death penalty. They do not consider it a factor worth mentioning.[23]

One prison warden has said that in his twenty years in that profession, he has never seen a single criminal who would have refrained from using a gun because of any idea that he might get the death sentence. "The criminal's fear of the gallows," he said, "is a fairy story built up by well-meaning people to deter others. We could build up just as effective a hoax about the horrors of life imprisonment if it were our wish."[24]

The stable, normal person is held back from committing murder by moral feelings that have been developed in him since early childhood. Legal sanctions—whether capital or other— are only a secondary and for most persons quite unnecessary reinforcement of the moral prohibition. It takes an abnormal mind to commit a killing. This is worth emphasizing. In detective stories, any person who had a motive and opportunity is a suspect, and the actual killer always turns out to be someone who, except for this one excursion into murder, has led an exemplary life. That isn't the way it happens in real life. A person who has lived a decent, balanced life doesn't suddenly murder his Uncle Jonathan in order to inherit his estate. In cases where something of the sort seemed to have happened, investigation will show that the murderer had long been that kind of person.

Whereas the law—like the detective story writer— tends to regard the criminal as a man who at a given point in time intentionally and of his free will decided to commit a wrongful act, the psychologist sees the act as the culmination of an enormous variety of forces extending far back into the past. Murderous impulses often go back to early impulses of suicide, sadism or masochism.[25] We all bear certain emotional scars from our early childhood, some much worse than others. Some of these early influences, which Sheldon and Eleanor Glueck deem weighty enough to be used as social predictive factors for predicting delinquency, are:

1. discipline of boy by father
2. supervision of boy by mother

3. affection of father for boy
4. affection of mother for boy
5. cohesiveness of family.[26]

A high percentage of murderers are not only emotionally scarred and twisted, but are actually psychotic. In England, of the patients in Broadmoor, the institution for the criminal insane, over fifty percent are murder cases, and another 20 to 25 percent are persons who attempted murder. Of persons suspected of murder, in 1946-47 35 percent attempted suicide before arrest. Some 22 percent actually do commit suicide. Of those brought to trial, over 50 percent are found either too mentally disordered to stand trial, or if tried, are found guilty but insane. Another 4 percent are subsequently certified as insane.[27] These figures indicate that mental disorder is the predominant factor in murder. Studies in this country tend to support the same conclusion. In fact, Bernard C. Glueck, Jr. has said, "It is my personal opinion, based on the examination of men in the death house at Sing Sing, that no person in our society is in a normal state of mind when he commits a murder."[28]

The argument that abolishing the death penalty would encourage a terrible crime wave is an old one. It has been raised every time we abolished the death penalty for each of the scores, and even hundreds, of other crimes formerly so punishable.[29] The pattern is always the same. A movement to abolish capital punishment for a given crime is met by dire forebodings, mainly from the judges, that abolition would result in a dangerous increase in the crime in question. Then, after abolition, there is a remarkable absence of any such increase.

In 1810, Sir Samuel Romilly introduced a bill into the House of Commons to abolish capital punishment for the theft of five shillings or over from a shop. Chief Justice Lord Ellenborough opposed the bill. He said: "I trust your lordships will pause before you assent to an experiment pregnant with danger to the security of property, and before you repeal a statute which has so long been held necessary for public security. I am convinced with the rest of the Judges, public expediency requires there should be no remission of the terror denounced against this description of offenders. Such will be the consequences of the repeal of this statute that I am certain depredations to an unlimited extent would be immediately committed." Lord Ellenborough spoke for all his colleagues on the bench. Not a single judge or magistrate supported the bill. It failed to pass.

In 1814, Romilly tried to persuade Parliament to substitute as the penalty for treason simple hanging instead of the then penalty of hanging, being cut down while still alive, disembowelled, decapitated and quartered. That, notice, was less than a century and a half ago. Parliament refused to pass the bill. Apparently they concurred in the statement of one of the members that the bill was a "mischievous attempt 'to unsettle public opinion with respect to the enormity of these atrocious offenses.' "[30]

Eventually both of these reforms were enacted. "Depredations of an unlimited extent" were not immediately committed. Public opinion was not unsettled. None of the predictions of dire consequences came true. But the same kind of predictions continued to be made, by the same kind of armchair criminologists.

Mr. Justice Frankfurter has said of members of the legal profession that "the most eminent among them, for a hundred years, have testified with complete confidence that something is impossible which, once it is introduced, is found to be very easy of administration. The history of legal procedure is the history of rejection of reasonable and civilized standards in the administration of law by most eminent judges and leading practitioners."[31]

Investiture in high office, as judge, legislator or prosecutor, does not magically endow a man with scholarly training and competence in criminology. It is necessary to say this because the public too often assumes the contrary. The honorable gentlemen's pronouncements are assumed to be the product of many years of experience and study, when in fact they may be based on a few not necessarily typical cases, or even on nothing whatever except emotional reflexes. Lord Ellenborough was Chief Justice of the King's Bench and a legal scholar. But his pronouncements on the necessity of retaining the death penalty expressed merely a personal predilection not based on any data whatever. Equally baseless assertions continue to be made by his professional descendants to this day.

Opponents of abolition are always quick to cite atrocious cases and ask what we would do about them. Only last year, a judge of the Ontario Court of Appeal answered the advocates of abolition at a Toronto forum on the subject by asking: "What about men like O'Donnell who raped and strangled to death Ruth Taylor under conditions of indescribable horror . . .? or Hutson . . . who was convicted on the clearest possible evidence of murdering a little girl of three years by a brutal, bestial attack during which she was virtually disembowelled? Or the three monsters . . . who literally fried to death a schoolteacher who lived alone, in order to make her reveal the whereabouts of her life savings?"[32]

Recalling such cases raises the hackles and the blood pressure. But what do they prove about the wisdom of retaining or abolishing the death penalty? All these cases happened in the judge's own jurisdiction, which *retains* the death penalty. Obviously capital punishment for the first of these cases did not prevent commission of the second, or the third.

Across the line from the Canadian province of Ontario is the State of Michigan, which abolished capital punishment more than a hundred years ago. It has consistently had a smaller number of murders per hundred thousand of population than its neighboring states of Illinois, Indiana and Ohio.[33] It would be invalid to conclude from this that abolition reduces the incidence of crime. But it is valid and correct to conclude that the death penalty is not more of a deterrent than other forms of punishment that might be substituted for it.

With all deference to judges, it seems proper to say

that the deterrent effect of any given punishment can be calculated, if at all, only by someone having "extensive acquaintance with psychological *norms,* with the effectiveness of distant anxiety as an inhibiting force, with the after-history of every variety of behavioristic disorder, to say nothing of an expert knowledge of statistics and of statistical method."[34]

Psychiatrists have paid relatively little attention to the validity or fallacy of the "deterrent" effect of the death penalty, and have largely been content to leave such investigations to the sociologists and penal reformers. Yet students of the mind should find interesting this phenomenon of the continued repetition of the stock arguments in favor of capital punishment, not only by the man in the street but by eminent lawyers and judges—in spite of the fact that there is no evidence to support them. Does this not suggest the propriety of a psychological examination into the existence of some unconscious roots to this urge to punish, some sadistic impulses perhaps, and perhaps some unconscious guilts.

Today we have pretty generally abolished the death penalty for all crimes except murder. Why this one great exception? Why should a punishment that did not deter men from stealing sheep be any more effective to deter them from committing murder? Murder usually involves less calm premeditation, not more. Punishment or the threat of it is more likely to deter crimes where there is a conscious and deliberate motive for gain. It is least likely to deter crimes attributable to passion, and to embittered, frustrated or actually disordered personality.

Perhaps the reason is that we regard murder with peculiar horror, as the "crime of crimes." But that view of murder is certainly not universal. The anthropologists tell us that most people throughout most of recorded history have regarded various other crimes as more abhorrent and more socially dangerous than killing—incest, for example. And some of us today would be willing to agree with our primitive ancestors that there are worse crimes than murder. Is the person who at one crisis in his life commits a sudden killing worse than the one who makes it his daily business to peddle dope to teen-agers? Introducing a person to the dope habit not only destroys him physically but morally as well, yet it is done deliberately and cold-bloodedly, by persons who know and who count on the fact that once the victim is "hooked" he will almost certainly never break the habit, but will be reduced to lying, stealing and almost every possible crime, to get the money to buy dope.

I am not proposing that we make dope peddling a capital offense. I am pointing out the incongruity of our retaining the death penalty for one crime although we have abolished it for most, of retaining it for a primitive and today not socially threatening form of crime, although we do not extend it to newer crimes which are a real threat to our social organization.

But even if we agree that murder is the most wicked of crimes, that seems relevant only for a retributive theory of justice, not one based on deterrence. Today we don't like to say that we inflict punishment merely for vengeance. We say that we are doing it to deter repetition of the offense, either by the offender or by others who might otherwise be tempted to follow his example. So far as deterrence is concerned, the question is not so much whether murder creates a higher degree of moral revulsion, but rather, whether murderers are less likely to be deterred by imprisonment or other measures and more likely to be deterred by the threat of death.

Most murderers are not hardened criminals. Most of them fall into two classes, the pathological and the passionate. I have already cited the statistics showing how high a proportion fall into the pathological group. And most of the rest are people who killed in some momentary fit of passion.

A study of 1,000 murders committed in New Jersey revealed that 67 percent of them arose out of unpremeditated quarrels—with wives, mistresses, sex rivals or acquaintances. Even of the premeditated murders, most were also of wives, sweethearts, sex rivals. Only 18.8 percent were committed during other crimes such as robbery, burglary, rape and kidnapping. Another 3.1 percent were committed while resisting an officer.[35]

Murder is not typically the crime of the so-called criminal class. Much more often, it is an incident in miserable lives characterized by domestic quarrels, brawls, drinking and fighting. The killing is the unpremeditated and more or less accidental culmination of a long series of acts of violence. If the harshest penalty is ever needed as the strongest deterrent, it ought to be reserved for the professionals, the gangsters, the pickpockets, the safe-crackers, the confidence men. Not for the murderers. Yet of the really hardened criminals, the professionals, who are most likely to weigh the odds before they act, we find very few convicted of murder.

Police officials often argue that the threat of capital punishment deters criminals from carrying lethal weapons, or at least deters them from using them against the police when in danger of being arrested. Abolishing the death penalty, it is said, would therefore result in more policemen being killed or wounded. But the statistics reveal no factual basis for this assumption. The number of policemen killed is slightly smaller, proportionately, in the states that have abolished the death penalty than in those that retain it.[36]

Everyone who has made any study of the subject knows that it is not the severity of the punishment that is most important for deterrence; it is the certainty that punishment will actually result. The perfect penal system would be one that operates like a red hot stove; touch it and you get burned. It isn't necessary that the burn be fatal to induce people to keep their hands off. As Sir Walter Moberly said a few years ago, "... the most ferocious penalties are ineffective so long as prospective criminals believe they have a fair chance of escaping them. ... If he commits a murder he may not be caught; if caught he may not be convicted; if convicted he may still be reprieved. . . . Thus it is *certainty* rather than *severity* of punishment which really deters. . . . An increase in the efficiency of the police force does more to prevent murder than the busiest hangman."[37] For capital crimes, juries are notoriously reluctant to convict. This *reduces* the certainty of punishment and in consequence, its deterrent effect.

There are other objections to capital punishment beside the lack of evidence that it is any more of a deterrent than any other forms of punishment. Being irrevocable, it allows no opportunity for reversing a wrong conviction of an innocent man. It places on the officials who have to take part in an execution a hateful duty that even the advocates of capital punishment would not want to perform themselves and do not even want to witness. The executioner for New York and Pennsylvania suggested a few years ago that the judges who hand down the sentence should be required to witness its execution. I doubt whether most judges would want that. Warden Lewis E. Lawes of Sing Sing said that during all his term no judge and no prosecutor ever asked to witness the execution of a man they had prosecuted and sentenced.[38] But if executing wrongdoers were as effective a deterrent as its apologists claim, we should encourage—perhaps compel—not only judges and prosecutors but everybody to witness the act. We have given up public executions because we know the sight does not deter. It brutalizes people and makes them more callous toward killing.

Capital punishment is defeatist, because, contrary to

modern developments in penal reform it abandons the possibility of reforming the criminal and it has an adverse effect upon efforts to reform other prisoners in the institution at the time the execution takes place. These convicts, whom the prison regime is presumably trying to treat and to rehabilitate into society, identify with the condemned man, and they align themselves against the hateful, punishing society that takes his life. The whole principle of intimidation by fear appears actually to contribute to aggressive behavior in some persons. Capital punishment may serve as an actual incitement to crime in three types of cases:

1. The suicidal group. Some depressed patients take the attitude that death is a just punishment for their imagined sins, and murder is a means of securing it.

2. Those to whom the lure of danger has a strong appeal; possibly a large group. The danger of capital punishment may act as an actual incentive to acts like robbery with violence.

3. The exhibitionist group. The exhibitionist wishes "for a time successfully to pit his wits against the police, but that would not satisfy him unless he was in the end caught; because otherwise nobody would know how clever he had been in outwitting the law so long. So that we can't think the exhibitionist would be expected to give himself up after his first crime; but sooner or later he would so arrange things that he was found out and had the satisfaction of a spectacular trial."[39] These persons do not usually carry their activities to the point

of committing crimes that may lead to the death penalty, although even that occurs at times.

The death penalty probably also increases the cost of criminal trials. I say probably because this is largely an unexplored question. But it is probably true that persons charged with capital crimes are less likely to plead guilty than they would be if the crime were not capital. And avoiding a drawn out criminal trial by a plea of guilty saves the state several thousand dollars. The money so saved could be better used to pay the salaries of parole and probation officers in a constructive effort to prevent crime. In 1931, after a Pennsylvania capital trial, a social worker in Reading said: "It cost the State of Pennsylvania $23,658 to prosecute, convict and electrocute Irene Schroeder at the Western Penitentiary. If one-twentieth of this sum had been spent ten years ago by any social workers on that 22-year-old girl, that electrocution would have been prevented."[40]

Another way capital punishment increases the costs of trial is by increasing the time needed to obtain a jury. Jurors as already said are reluctant to serve where they have to send a man to his death. In notorious cases, this may cause fantastic delays—several days spent in interrogating from one to two hundred veniremen before a jury is obtained. The effect that this kind of sifting out of those most reluctant to convict of capital crime may have upon verdicts is another unexplored field.

The death penalty may actually make convictions harder to obtain. It is always necessary to present a very

convincing case to obtain a conviction where the penalty
is death. When lesser penalties are possible, the rate of
convictions rises rapidly. When forgery was a capital
offense in England, juries in the 18th century began to
revolt, and simply refused to convict. As a result, we had
the anomalous situation of the banks appealing to Parliament (in vain) to abolish the death penalty.[41] That
probably gives one explanation for the fact that, whereas
in 1918 twelve states made the death penalty mandatory
on conviction of a capital offense, today only Vermont
does so.[42]

In spite of all the controversy concerning it, the death
penalty is so rarely resorted to that it hardly figures as
an actual penal practice. In the whole United States,
there are today only a little over one hundred executions for murder per year, although there are about
7,000 murders per year; the rest are given prison terms
if they are convicted at all.[43] By dividing the crime into
degrees and by giving the judge or the jury discretion in
imposing sentence, we have in practice substantially
reduced the number of capital sentences that otherwise
would be passed. The same trend is going on everywhere
else throughout the civilized world. Scotland in a period
of fifty years had six hundred murders, yet only twenty-
three executions, mainly because of the operation of the
Scotch doctrine of diminished responsibility.[44] In England the device used is mainly that of the exercise of the
prerogative of mercy. In other countries where the
death penalty has not been abolished, it is falling into
desuetude by administrative practice. In Belgium, for

example, although the death penalty is still on the statute books there has not actually been an execution since
1863. A sanction so rarely applied can hardly be regarded as an operative instrument of penal policy.[45]

Where it is applied, it is applied in a shockingly hap-
hazard and discriminatory way. Of the few who are
actually executed, almost all are poor, almost all are
men, and a disproportionately high number are Negroes.
Defendants of wealth or education practically never go
to the gallows or the electric chair. Neither do women.
Warden Lawes of Sing Sing escorted 150 persons to their
death. Of them, 150 were poor; 149 were men.[46] During
the twenty years from 1930 to 1950, there were 3,029
executions in the United States. Of these, 21 were
women. And of these few, the majority were Negro
women. In the southern states where capital punishment
is retained for rape, it is used almost exclusively against
Negroes. This is so flagrantly true that it was made the
basis of an argument of discrimination by the NAACP
in the notorious "Martinsville Rape Case" of 1950. The
Association's brief on appeal cited figures, which have
never been questioned, showing that although 809 white
men had been convicted of rape since 1909, not one had
been executed. During the same period 54 Negroes were
executed on rape convictions.[47]

Thirty years ago, a House Committee recommended
favorably on a bill to abolish the death penalty in the
District of Columbia. It said:

As it is now applied the death penalty is nothing but an arbitrary discrimination against an occasional victim. It can-

not even be said that it is reserved as a weapon of retributive justice for the most atrocious criminals. For it is not necessarily the most guilty who suffer it. Almost any criminal with wealth or influence can escape it but the poor and friendless convict, without means or power to fight his case from court to court or to exert pressure upon the pardoning executive, is the one singled out as a sacrifice to what is little more than a tradition.[48]

The bill did not pass. But what the committee said is at least as true today as it was then.

Warden Lewis E. Lawes said twenty years ago:

Capital punishment in the United States may be regarded as practically abolished through indifferent enforcement. But, by retaining the death penalty in its penal codes, it necessarily goes through the theatricals of the threat of enforcement. These very theatricals lend glamor to the accused fighting for his life. The offense, no matter how heinous, is frequently disregarded in the new drama portrayed in the courtroom where prosecutors demand death for the prisoners and counsel pleads for mercy. These theatricals reach out beyond the courtroom and weaken law enforcement all along the line.[49]

They distort the administration of justice, producing unmerited acquittals in some cases and in others convictions not justified by an unemotional evaluation of the evidence.

But the main argument against capital punishment is not concerned with what it does or fails to do to criminals. It concerns what it does to the rest of us. Capital punishment does more harm in brutalizing and lowering the moral standard of the community as a whole than it does good by eliminating a few dangerous individuals.

It becomes for many people an absorbing and unhealthy fascination to follow the trial of a person on trial for his life. "Public interest of an almost prurient nature heightens under the influence of the modern media of mass communication. There seems to be released among us a perverted curiosity verging on mass sadism which crowds the trial courts and surrounds the place of execution. Unhappy and unpleasant emotions are stirred in most of us."[50]

As Mr. Justice Frankfurter said: "When life is at hazard in a trial, it sensationalizes the whole thing almost unwittingly; the effect on juries, the Bar, the public, the judiciary, I regard as very bad. I think scientifically the claim of deterrence is not worth much. Whatever proof there may be in my judgment does not outweigh the social loss due to the inherent sensationalism of a trial for life."[51] In England, Viscount Templewood said: "It makes people gloat over crime and I think, however much you safeguard the actual carrying out of executions, they also pander to those morbid feelings that lie very near the surface in most of us and that would be much better repressed."[52]

We have mentioned the sensational murder trial held in Lancaster, Pennsylvania. A college student was charged with murdering a young woman. There hadn't been a death sentence in Lancaster County since 1922, but this case aroused all the old morbid curiosity and animosity. On the day of the opening of the trial the crowd began to form in the alley behind the court house as early as 6:00 A.M. By nine o'clock the lines stretched from the rear of the court house down the alley all the way to the next street and around the corner. A policeman later said there were at least five hundred people.

The crowd kept coming every day of the trial. In the morning, when the accused was brought in, and in the afternoon, when he was taken away, the crowd was so dense that police had difficulty getting through to the waiting vehicles. People shouted out words of encouragement or of condemnation. Some struggled to get a better look, others wanted to lay their hands on him. One woman brushed his sleeve with her fingertips. "I touched him," she said with her face bright, "that's enough for me—I touched him." On the last day some were weeping, some were praying, some were shouting.[53]

Part of the crowd interest may have been stimulated by the brutality of the crime and the implications of sexual attack. And part of it may have been spurred by the local press. The defendant's attorney, in later preparing an appeal, compiled a list of what he called inflammatory material taken from the three Lancaster papers. But that material wasn't particularly garish— nothing like the really lurid whipping up of morbid public curiosity that you have in other cities where some of the newspapers are much worse, as in New York, or where they're all worse, as in Los Angeles.

The basic value of our civilization is, in Albert Schweitzer's phrase, Reverence for Life. Indeed, a good measure of any civilization is the extent to which this seminal concept is valued and implemented. If we want to inculcate respect for human life, we must not ourselves take life in the name of the law.

Official killing by the state makes killing respectable. It not merely dulls the sensibilities of people to cruelty and inhumanity, but actively stimulates cruelty. It negates the efforts of those who are working to stimulate the better instincts of men.

And let us not forget that in a democratic society the state is you and I. It is not an impersonal, inhuman machine that executes these persons. It is you and I who provide the money to erect the gallows or install the electric chair. It is you and I who pay the executioner to act as our representative. The execution of a condemned man is not a stage play, to be read about in the newspapers. It is a deliberated act in which every citizen participates.

And while Gallup polls have shown that about half of the people in the United States favor retaining capital punishment, it is interesting to observe that they don't like the idea of having anything to do with it themselves. We don't reveal the identity of the executioner because we know that he would be generally shunned by his neighbors if they knew his secret. One reason why execution by intravenous injection is not practical is that it would require a doctor to administer, and doctors want no part in the business. If we were honest with ourselves we would have to admit that we are ashamed of keeping capital punishment as a part of our penal system. In our hearts we agree with Viscount

Templewood who said in his book, *The Shadow of the Gallows,* "The whole act from start to finish is repulsive and unworthy of a civilized community."

The driving force behind the movement for abolition has been democracy. Only Fascism halted the trend in countries like Italy, Austria and Germany. Democracy has fostered it, in Europe, in South America, in Australia—everywhere except in the United States.

Only in this country is there no organized political movement for abolition. No American state has abolished the death penalty since 1917. It isn't even the subject of political discussion here, as it is right now in England and in Canada. Here, it is a subject for high school debaters—nothing more. As long as abolition has no political champion, no organized voice in the forum of public discussion, we in America are failing to move along with the current of civilized thinking.

If and when we do renounce the illusory protection of the death penalty, we should not make the mistake of merely shifting our faith to imprisonment or any other negative sanction as a remedy for crime. Let us hope that abolition will lead us rather to provide more *preventive* law enforcement. As Thomas Fuller said more than two hundred years ago, "To punish and not prevent is to labor at the pump and leave open the leak." One way to get more preventive law enforcements is by increasing police efficiency. It was increased efficiency in enforcement that cut short the wave of kidnappings for ransom in the 1930's, rather than the adoption of laws authorizing the death penalty for this crime.[54] But the best way to prevent crime is to identify potential criminals and guide them away from an antisocial career before they carry that career to a tragic climax. It can be done. It is being done by agencies such as the Diagnostic Center at Menlo Park, New Jersey, and the New York City Youth Board.[55]

With the help of insights that psychiatry and psychology are giving us into how the mainsprings of human behavior operate, we are learning much about how to bring up children to fit into the world. Perhaps we are also learning how to build a world fit for them to live in. With these insights, we are better armed for the task of molding a society that nurtures the healthy and fruitful growth of individual life, a society that holds inviolable the dignity of man and fosters love and understanding of one's fellow man rather than hostility and aggression—a society, in short, that respects life.

Notes

NOTES TO CHAPTER I

1. For a discussion and illustration of the confusion the use of the word "insanity" has caused, see Weihofen, *Mental Disorder as a Criminal Defense* (1954) pp. 4-6. Dr. Isaac Ray a century ago, in his discussions of the tests of criminal "insanity," tended to confuse the issue, skipping back and forth between two meanings of the words: (1) what we today would call mental disorder or mental disease, and (2) such degree of mental disorder as will relieve the person of criminal responsibility. Ray, *The Medical Jurisprudence of Insanity* (3rd ed., 1855); Ray, "The Law of Insanity," 4 *Am. L. Rev.* 236, 246-47 (1870).

This kind of confusion was aided by the fact that "insanity" was the term used by the medical profession a hundred years ago to mean what in current phraseology is called mental disorder, psychosis, or mental disease. To some extent, "insanity" is still so used in England. In this country, and also largely in England, the term has been abandoned in psychiatry, and psychiatrists are prone to insist that it is "exclusively a legal term." But it is at best an ambiguous legal term, and the fact that old cases are still cited in which it was used as a medical term compounds the ambiguity.

The Canadian Mental Health Association has recommended abolition in the law of such terms as "insanity." Special Committee on Bill No. 93, Minutes of Proceedings and Evidence, No. 5, p. 181.

An excellent statement of the distinction between mental disorder and criminal responsibility is that of the late Professor Jerome Michael, "Psychiatry and the Criminal Law," 21 *Am. Bar Assn. J.* 271 (1935). See also Waelder, "Psychiatry and the Problem of Criminal Responsibility," 101 *U. Pa. L. Rev.* 378 (1952).

2. Not all modern psychiatrists agree that the difference between normality and abnormality is merely quantitative. Some hold to the view that there is a qualitative difference, but probably a majority today accept the quantitative view. The two views are succinctly stated in the Encyclopaedia Britannica, "Abnormal Psychology," (1955):

"Relationship between Normal and Abnormal.—From ancient times down to the present there have been two diametrically opposed views with regard to this important problem. According to one, there is a clean break, a chasm, between normal and abnormal. The normal person, it is contended, cannot possibly put himself in the place of abnormal persons and see things from their perspectives. According to the other view, there is unbroken continuity between normal and abnormal (principle of continuity). That is, the normal shades imperceptibly into the abnormal, and both share a borderland in which normality and abnormality cannot with certainty be distinguished.

"The absolutist tradition, which sharply divides abnormal from normal behaviour, finds popular expression in such statements as that a person is out of his head, has lost his reason or his mind, and therefore needs an alienist; *i.e.*, a specialist who deals with the mentally estranged. Most 19th-century alienists and nerve specialists, the predecessors of modern psychiatrists, accepted this hypothesis of discontinuity as fact. They tried to give substance to the speculations by postulating hypothetical brain and nerve changes in their patients to parallel the behaviour deviations which they observed. Early in the 20th century it was demonstrated conclusively that general paresis is the result of a specific brain infection. This raised the hope among absolutists that some day all neuroses and psychoses might prove to be no more than diseases of the brain. Their hope during the intervening four decades failed to materialize. . . . The relativist tradition, which maintains that there is continuity between normal and abnormal behaviour, did not become dominant in behaviour pathology until the 20th century. The position of the relativists was greatly strengthened by the growing realization, late in the 18th century and throughout the 19th, that abnormal phenomena could be deliberately induced for a short time in normal persons. . . ."

3. "In former times when juries were ignorant, experts unknown, and counsel not allowed to speak for the prisoner in relation to any matter of fact, courts were obliged, in justice to the latter, to

instruct the jury respecting matters of fact, and especially was this so in cases involving questions of insanity. In a criminal trial, the jury had no means of learning how this disease affects the mind, for they had nothing to guide them but such views as the counsel for the Crown chose to impart. They naturally looked to the court for direction, and the court, standing in the relation of counsel for the prisoner, gave them such information as it had obtained from the best books and the most eminent physicians of the time." Ray, "The Law of Insanity," 4 *Am. L. Rev.* 248 (1870). See also 63 *Yale L. J.* 189-190, 190-191. One of Dr. Ray's earliest strictures on the subject was written in 1835. Ray, "Criminal Law of Insanity," 14 *Am. Jurist* 253 (1835).

4. Ray, *The Medical Jurisprudence of Insanity* (3rd ed., 1855) §41, p. 58.

5. Overholser, "Pioneers in Psychiatry: Isaac Ray," 45 *J. Crim. L. & Criminology.* 249 (1954).

6. Pound, *Formative Era of American Law* (1938) 4, 30-31, quoted in Note, "Doe of New Hampshire: Reflections on a Nineteenth Century Judge," 63 *Harv. L. Rev.* 513 (1950). See also Hening, *Eight Great American Lawyers* (1909).

7. Reik, *The Doe-Ray Correspondence: A Pioneer Collaboration in the Jurisprudence of Mental Disease*, 63 *Yale L. J.* 183 (1953).

8. 47 N. H. 120.

9. *State* v. *Pike*, 49 N. H. 399 (1869).

10. *State* v. *Jones,* 50 N. H. 369 (1871). "On the issue of insanity, Judge Ladd stated, the jury must be satisfied beyond a reasonable doubt that the killing was not produced by mental disease to find the defendant guilty. Then he deepened the analysis of Judge Doe. The ultimate question, he said, was whether the accused, at the time of the act, had the mental capacity to entertain a criminal intent. All symptoms were to be weighed by the jury in considering whether the act was the offspring of insanity: 'if it was, a criminal intent did not produce it; if it was not, a criminal intent did produce it and it was a crime.' Under this analysis it would seem that the extent to which the mental disorder reduces the possibility of forming a criminal intent would be the extent to which the disorder may be said to have caused the act." (Foot-

notes omitted.) Note, "Criminal Responsibility and Mental Disorder: New Approaches to an Old Problem," 30 *Ind. L. J.* 194, 203 (1955).

11. 214 F. 2d 862 (1954).

12. This last paragraph of the opinion contains the only reference to a relationship between mental disorder and lack of criminal intent. Apparently the court in the Durham case has not adopted the rationale of the New Hampshire court in *State* v. *Jones,* supra, note 10, that if the act was the offspring of mental disease, then it was not produced by a criminal intent.

It has been suggested that: "One reason why the Durham court refused to go as far as Judge Ladd may be found in the brief of the *Amicus Curiae,* p. 30-31, *Stewart* v. *United States,* 214 F. 2d 879 (D. C. Cir. 1954), filed by Abraham Chayes. It suggests that the disease-intent relationship, if literally applied, might result in more severity than the M'Naghten Rules, if 'intent' is not conceived as the product of the total personality. Incapacity to form intent may be just another symptom of disease, which would confuse the expert and distort the issues for the jury. 'This second formulation of the New Hampshire test seems designed to insure that only serious or advanced mental disorders will be effective to confer immunity from punishment. If this is so, the end is better served and with less confusion by incorporating the requirement of serious disorder in the first version of the test [did the disease produce the act]. That would then require the jury to say whether the defendant was suffering from severe mental disorder of which the act charged was a consequence. So limited, the test could not be considered too lenient.' " Note, 30 *Ind. L. J.* 194, 204-5 (1955).

13. The *Index to Legal Periodicals* lists no less than forty-one law reviews that had printed articles or comments on the Durham case.

NOTES TO CHAPTER II

1. American Law Institute, Model Penal Code, Tentative Draft No. 4, p. 156 (1955).

2. 10 Clark & Fin. 200.

3. The right-and-wrong test is the *sole* test of responsibility in Arizona, California, Florida, Georgia, Idaho, Iowa, Kansas, Loui-

siana, Maine, Maryland, Minnesota, Mississippi, Missouri, Nebraska, Nevada, New Jersey, New York, North Carolina, North Dakota, Oklahoma, Oregon, Pennsylvania, South Carolina, South Dakota, Tennessee, Texas, Washington, West Virginia and Wisconsin. It is the primary test, supplemented only by the irresistible-impulse test, in all the remaining jurisdictions except New Hampshire and the District of Columbia. For citations to cases and statutes, see Weihofen, *Mental Disorder as a Criminal Defense,* pp. 50-52, 129-173 (1954).

4. John Biggs, Jr., *The Guilty Mind,* p. 107 (1955).

5. Id., p. 108.

6. Hadfield's case, 27 How. St. Trials 1282 (1800) was probably the most famous case tried prior to M'Naghten's case. James Hadfield was a veteran of many wars. He had sustained terrible head wounds in battle which caused his head to hang down as though it had been "almost disevered," and had been discharged from the army on the ground of insanity. It seems that he was suffering from systematized delusions that, like the Saviour, he was ordained to sacrifice himself for the world's salvation. In order to be executed to attain this end, he shot at King George III, that by the appearance of crime, he might be condemned and so perform the sacrifice he felt divinely called to make. He was defended by Lord Erskine who, although he stated that he accepted the principles previously laid down by Coke and Hale, questioned the interpretation of those authorities which Crown counsel was urging in this case, that those authorities required a total deprivation of memory to protect a man from criminal responsibility. "If a *total deprivation of memory* was intended by these great lawyers to be taken in the *literal* sense of the word," Erskine declared, "then no such madness ever existed in the world." Id. p. 1312.

There are extreme cases, he admitted, where "the human mind is stormed in its citadel and laid prostrate under the stroke of frenzy." Such cases, however, are rare and can present no judicial difficulty. But "in other cases, Reason is not driven from her seat, but distraction sits down upon it along with her, holds her trembling upon it, and frightens her from her propriety." Such persons, said Erskine, are subject to delusions. In some cases, these delusions are so terrific as wholly to overpower the faculties; in others, they are more circumscribed, yet the disordered imagination still holds the most uncontrollable dominion over reality and fact, "and these are the cases which frequently mock the wisdom of the wisest in judicial trials because such persons often reason with a subtlety which puts in the shade the ordinary conception of mankind; the conclusions are just, and frequently profound; but the premises from which they reason, when within the range of the malady, are uniformly false." Id. p. 1313-14.

"In substance," says Judge Biggs, "Erskine, in Hadfield's defense, advanced the theory that a man could know right from wrong, could understand the nature of the act he was about to commit, could manifest a clear design and foresight and cunning in planning and executing it, but if his mental condition produced or was the cause of the criminal act, he should not be held legally responsible for it." Biggs, *The Guilty Mind,* p. 89 (1955).

7. A popular description of faculty psychology and its forerunner, phrenology, is found in Karl Stern's *The Third Revolution,* p. 47 ff. (1954).

8. "When the word 'psychology' was coined, two hundred years ago, it was supposed that the two-worlds legend was true. It was supposed, in consequence, that since Newtonian science explains (it was erroneously thought) everything that exists and occurs in the physical world, there could and should be just one other counterpart science explaining what exists and occurs in the postulated non-physical world. As Newtonian scientists found and examined their data in visual, auditory and tactual perception, so psychologists would find and examine their counterpart data by counterpart, non-visual, non-auditory, non-tactual perception. . . .

"Abandonment of the two-worlds legend involves the abandonment of the idea that there is a locked door and a still to be discovered key. Those human actions and reactions, those spoken and unspoken utterances, those tones of voice, facial expressions and gestures, which have always been the data of all the other students of men, have, after all, been the right and the only manifestations to study. They and they alone have merited, but fortunately not received, the grandiose title 'mental phenomena'. . . .

"Chemists once tried to find out the properties of phlogiston, but, as they never captured any phlogiston, they reconciled themselves to studying instead its influences and outward manifestations. They examined, in fact, the phenomena of combustion and soon abandoned the postulate of an uninspectable heat-stuff. The postulation of it had been a will-o'-the-wisp, the sort of will-o'-the-wisp that encourages the adventurous to explore uncharted thickets and then, ungratefully, to chart the thickets in maps that make no further mention of those false beacons. Psychological research work will not have been wasted if the postulate of a special mind-stuff goes the same way." G. Ryle, *The Concept of Mind,* pp. 319-20, 320-21, 322 (1949).

9. J. Z. Young, *Doubt and Certainty in Science* (1951) pp. 97, 104.

10. The Greeks knew better. Plato, more than 2,300 years ago, quoted Socrates as saying on the basis of his experiences in the Greek army, "For this is the great error of our day in the treatment of the human body, that physicians separate the soul from the body." Quoted by Henson,"Psychosomatic Aspects of Personal Injuries," 23 *Tenn. L. Rev.* 622 (1955).

11. "It has for a long time been taken for an indisputable axiom that the Mind is in some important sense tripartite, that is, that there are just three ultimate classes of mental processes. The Mind or Soul, we are often told, has three parts, namely, Thought, Feeling and Will; or, more solemnly, the Mind or Soul functions in three irreducibly different modes, the Cognitive mode, the Emotional mode and the Conative mode. This traditional dogma is not only not self-evident, it is such a welter of confusions and false inferences that it is best to give up any attempt to re-fashion it. It should be treated as one of the curios of theory. . . .

"It will be clear why I reject this story. It is just an inevitable extension of the myth of the ghost in the machine. It assumes that there are mental states and processes enjoying one sort of existence, and bodily states and processes enjoying another." Ryle, op. cit., pp. 62, 63.

12. Judge Thurman Arnold, in *Holloway* v. *United States,* 148 F. 2d 665, 667 (1945).

13. Overholser, *The Psychiatrist and the Law* (1953) p. 11.

14. Ray, *The Medical Jurisprudence of Insanity,* §248, pp. 259-60 (3d ed., 1855).

15. East, *Society and the Criminal,* pp. 20-21 (1951).

16. Glueck and Glueck, *Unraveling Juvenile Delinquency,* p. 215 (1950).

17. Cardozo, *What Medicine Can Do for the Law*, p. 32 (1930).

Long before Freud, Francis Bacon, a lawyer, said, "Numberless are . . . the ways, and sometimes inscrutable, in which the affections color and affect the understanding"; and "a man's disposition and the secret working of his mind are better discovered when he is in trouble than at other times." Quoted by Judge Jerome N. Frank, "Judicial Fact-Finding and Psychology," 14 *Ohio St. L. J.* 183, 189 (1953).

18. Sobeloff, "Insanity and the Criminal Law: From McNaghten to Durham, and Beyond," 41 *Am. Bar Assn. J.* 793 (1955), reprinted in 15 *Md. L. Rev.* 93 (1955).

19. "Mental abnormality is an exaggeration of normal attitudes and behavior. We all know people whom we consider over-sensitive or over-critical, unduly suspicious or excessively hostile and sarcastic, whom we recognize as too mild and meek for their own good or as overly assertive and demanding, or who are too much preoccupied with health and body functions, who tend to over-worry, over-drink, over-smoke, who are over-active or over-inhibited. We do not usually consider such people abnormal. Where do we draw the line? The line can be, and sometimes is, a thin one. The traits just listed are found in a varying extent in all of us. The difference is one of degree. The abnormal person is suffering from an intensification of these traits." Berliner, "Some Aspects of Mental Abnormality in Relation to Crime," 46 *J. Crim. L. & Criminology* 67, 68 (1955).

20. "If young lawyers were afforded the opportunity to have so-called "lie detector" or "narco-analytic" interviews with mentally healthy and mentally ill people, such interviews to be conducted jointly with an experienced psychiatrist, it would at once become apparent to both doctor and lawyer what is meant by "alteration of personality," as well as its indivisible unity. They would both at one and the same time be able to observe the frailty and illogical unity that is man, something that transgresses formalistic definitions." Zilboorg, *The Psychology of the Criminal Act and Punishment*, p. 44 (1954).

21. Roche, "Criminal Responsibility," in Hoch & Zubin, *Psychiatry and the Law*, p. 108 (1955).

22. Id.

23. Glueck and Glueck, *Unraveling Juvenile Delinquency,* pp. 288-9 (1950).

24. B. Glueck, "Changing Concepts in Forensic Psychiatry," 45 *J. Crim. L. & Criminology* 123, 131 (1954).

25. Zilboorg, *Mind, Medicine and Man,* p. 274 (1943).

26. "This leads to the central question: what are the forces of personality development that determine whether one resolves conflict in *acting* out in crime or in *living* out in mental illness? Both are regressively adaptive and are survival gestures in retreat from surrounding reality. In criminality one observes rebellion with destructive action directed outwardly; in mental illness, rebellion with destructive reaction absorbed inwardly. A complementarity is in this picture; it would seem that many criminals are compelled to repeat unlawful acts in order to preserve their sanity, and many law-abiding persons go crazy to avoid crime. From a social standpoint, mental illness has a higher premium in the sense that it spares the group at the expense of the individual. It would appear that the mentally ill person who commits a crime is cursed by a double failure of adaptation. His mental disintegration does not go far enough to nullify the remaining ego which on its own becomes a compliant accessory to his latent unlawful drives. Our hospitals are filled with people whose latent 'crimes' are lived out in the disguise of symbols and allegory. In them criminal drives lie behind a bizarre façade of social incapacity. In extreme cases imminent outward attack is often turned on the self in suicide. Such are those who take flight from surrounding reality rather than make outright attack upon it." Philip Q. Roche, "Criminality and Mental Illness—Two Faces of the Same Coin," 22 *U. Chi. L. Rev.* 320, 323 (1955).

NOTES TO CHAPTER III

1. Royal Commission on Capital Punishment, 1949-1953, Report, Memorandum of Dissent by Dame Florence Hancock, Mr. McDonald and Mr. Radzinowicz, pp. 285, 287.

2. Lawyers generally admit that in addition to persons who do not know right from wrong, there are others who are mentally ill, and whose illness is manifested primarily by impairment of voli-

tional capacity. But in most states, such impairment is not a legal defense, even when it exists in such extreme degree that the impulse to act can be called irresistible. Why not? Surely the law should not punish people for what they cannot avoid doing. No. The law denies this defense for a wholly practical reason—difficulty of proof. "Until the doctors can prove to one another's satisfaction when uncontrollable impulse does and, what is more important, when it does not exist, the stricter rule will probably be followed." A. L. Goodhart, *Essays in Jurisprudence and the Common Law,* pp. 47-48 (1931).

The assumption in Prof. Goodhart's statement is that we avoid this difficulty of proof by adhering to the right-and-wrong test; that that test is without comparable difficulty. But in fact there is just as much difficulty of proof in that test. "Factually there is no clear line of demarcation between delusion and normal rationalization. Doctors will vary tremendously in what they take to be reasonable exaggeration or fantasy and psychotic delusions. Yet juristic theory is willing to pretend that this distinction is a fairly easy one. On the other hand, jurisprudence has set aside the problem of compulsion until the doctors can agree." Edward S. Robinson, *Law and the Lawyers,* p. 75 (1935).

3. Codere's case, 12 Cr. App. R. 21 (1916). Some American cases, especially in Minnesota, Nebraska and North Dakota, use the word "nature" only—not "nature and quality." For citations to cases see Weihofen, *Mental Disorder as a Criminal Defense,* pp. 71-72 (1954).

4. Id., pp. 70, 73.

5. *Comm.* v. *Smith,* 374 Pa. 220, 97 A. 2d 25 (1953).

6. ". . . a child of moderate brightness will say that he hit his sister on the head, that she bled and that she fell; he will even admit that she died or that he killed her and will perhaps say that he was wrong to kill his sister. The criminal code does not accept this knowledge as valid; without knowing it the law recognizes here a fundamental medico-psychological distinction between the purely verbal knowledge which characterizes the child and the other type of knowledge which characterizes the adult. This fundamental difference between verbal or purely intellectual knowledge and the mysterious other kind of knowledge is familiar to every clinical psychiatrist; it is the difference between knowl-

edge divorced from affect and knowledge so fused with affect that it becomes a human reality." Zilboorg, "Misconceptions of Legal Insanity," 9 *Am. J. Orthopsychiatry* 540, 552 (1939). See also Bromberg and Cleckley, "The Medico-Legal Dilemma: A Suggested Solution," 42 *J. Crim. L. & Criminology* 729 (1952).

7. Prof. Jerome Hall is the leading exponent of this view. Hall, *General Principles of Criminal Law,* ch. 14, especially at pp. 523-24, 536-38. It is regrettable that Hall chooses to belittle and reject practically everything that has happened in psychology and psychiatry during the past hundred years, because of "the lack of agreement among psychologists," "the existence of many 'schools' of psychology," etc. Id. p. 485. Lack of agreement exists also in other fields of medicine, science, politics and economics, but we do not for that reason reject them in toto.

8. New York has held that "wrong" means "moral wrong," and that a person who acted under a delusion that the act was divinely commanded would not know that the act was "wrong." *People* v. *Schmidt,* 216 N. Y. 324, 110 N. E. 945 (1915). Tennessee and Texas cases have said that "wrong" means legal wrong merely. *Wason* v. *State,* 133 Tenn. 198, 180 S. W. 168 (1915); *McElroy* v. *State,* 146 Tenn. 442, 242 S. W. 883 (1922); *Harrison* v. *State,* 44 Tex. Crim. 164, 69 S. W. 500 (1902).

9. Glueck, *Mental Disorder and the Criminal Law,* p. 187 (1925).

10. "There is no developed scientific method of determining the existence of such 'knowledge' of the nature and quality or the right and wrong as related to an act, or the lack of it." Criminal Responsibility and Psychiatric Expert Testimony, The Committee on Psychiatry and Law of the Group For the Advancement of Psychiatry, Report No. 26, May 1954, p. 6.
"There is no objective method of determining in another 'knowledge' of the nature and quality or of the right or wrong related to behavior. . . . Furthermore no entities of mental disease can be abstracted out of matters solely confined to the cognitive faculty of knowledge as explicit in the test questions." Philip Q. Roche, "Criminal Responsibility," in Hoch and Zubin, *Psychiatry and the Law,* p. 107, at p. 113 (1955).

11. *Durham* v. *United States,* 214 F. 2d 862, 868 (1954).

12. Supra, note 10, at p. 5.

13. Waelder, "Psychiatry and the Problem of Criminal Responsibility," 101 *U. of Pa. L. Rev.* 378, at pp. 380-381 (1952).

14. R. Gehman, *A Murder in Paradise,* pp. 213-14 (1954).

15. West, "The Importance of Modern Psychiatry to the Lawyer," 14 *Ohio State L. J.* 138, 139 (1953).

16. Roche, op. cit. supra note 10, at p. 112.

17. John C. Whitehorn, quoted in Guttmacher and Weihofen, *Psychiatry and the Law,* p. 420 (1952).

18. *Durham* v. *United States,* 23- F. 2d 000 (1956). But again the conviction was reversed, this time because the trial judge, after telling the jury that if they found Durham not guilty by reason of insanity, he would be committed to St. Elizabeth's Hospital, added that "if the authorities adhere to their last opinion on this point he will be released very shortly."

19. Stephen, *History of the Criminal Law of England* (1st ed., 1883) vol. IV, p. 185.

20. Royal Commission on Capital Punishment, 1949-1953, Report, p. 113.

21. "I have tried enough of these cases to know that the question that the jury is going to ask itself is this: Ought the accused to be convicted under all the circumstances of the case? And if they decide he ought to be convicted, it won't make any difference what the experts say or what the judge charges. And if they decide it would not be just to convict him, they will turn him loose." Chief Judge John J. Parker of the United States Court of Appeals for the Fourth Circuit, Proceedings of the 32nd annual meeting of the American Law Institute, May 18-21, 1955, Washington, D. C., p. 216.
   The Australian experience is the same. "It can . . . be confidently affirmed that M'Naughten Rules are an elastic test, stretched or not in accordance with the jury's feeling of the 'madness' of the accused and the degree of detestation of his actions. If no logical and convincing motive for the killing is adduced, if medical evidence of mental disturbance supports the defence, and if the crime is not one that induces their deepest approbrium, juries will tend to apply the M'Naughten Rules with a benevolent width—otherwise they will not." Norval Morris, "Daniel

M'Naughten and the Death Penalty," 6 *Res Judicatae* 304, 335 (1954).

22. Royal Commission on Capital Punishment, 1949-1953, Report, p. 115.

23. John C. Whitehorn, "Psychiatry and Human Values," in Hoch and Zubin, *Psychiatry and the Law,* p. 144, at pp. 150-51 (1955).

24. Mr. Justice Hyman Barshay, "The Defense of Insanity in Criminal Cases," in Hoch and Zubin, *Psychiatry and the Law,* pp. 116, 120-21 (1955).

It has been suggested that the product rule "affords a greater degree of control over jury decisions. Whereas before it was well-nigh impossible for the trial judge or appellate court to review the jury finding of capacity in the defendant to 'know' that his act was wrong, the new rule calls for conclusions of fact which, at least in those extreme cases involving the manifestly psychotic, are subject to empirical verification and hence to revision or a new trial if the jury has exceeded the bounds of 'reasonableness.' " Warren P. Hill, "The Psychological Realism of Thurman Arnold," 22 *U. Chi. L. Rev.* 377, 392 (1955).

25. Schwartz, Punishment of Murder in Pennsylvania, Royal Commission on Capital Punishment, Memoranda and Replies to a Questionnaire received from Foreign and Commonwealth Countries (1952) pp. 776, 777. See *Comm.* v. *Daverse,* 364 Pa. 623, 73 A. 2d 405 (1950) and cases cited in Weihofen, *Mental Disorder as a Criminal Defense,* (1954) p. 162. But even if the Supreme Court has repudiated it, Prof. Schwartz says some trial judges in their instructions to juries still broaden the test to include it when they are so inclined.

26. In Ohio, the cases, although they extend back to 1834, leave it unclear whether irresistible impulse is or is not a defense. See *State* v. *Thompson,* Wright's Ohio Rep. 617, 622 (1834) (to be responsible, accused must have had "power to forbear or to do the act"); *Blackburn* v. *State,* 23 Ohio St. 146 (1873) (defendant must be a "free agent," with power to choose between right and wrong, and to avoid doing the act); *State* v. *Cumberworth,* 69 Ohio App. 239, 43 N. E. 2d 510 (1942) (irresistible impulse held no defense); *State* v. *Ross,* 92 Ohio App. 29, 108 N. E. 2d 77, appeal dismissed, 158 Ohio St. 248, 108 N. E. 2d 282 (1952) (same).

In New Mexico, whether irresistible impulse is a defense was uncertain until 1954, when it was held that it is. *State* v. *White,* 58 N. M. 324, 270 P. 2d 727 (1954).

27. "The person who acts on an irresistible impulse is really doing a non-volitional act; he is not knowing the nature and quality of his act in such a way as to form a rational judgment on that act, and that is a case of not knowing the act." Testimony of Dr. Ivison Russell, President, Royal Medico-Psychological Association, Minutes of Evidence, p. 485, Par. 6655. See also Jerome Hall, op. cit. supra., note 7.

28. During the nine years from 1940 through 1948, of persons proceeded against for murder in Scotland, twenty-one were found unfit to plead because of mental disorder, and only five were found to have committed the act but to have been mentally irresponsible at the time. Royal Commission on Capital Punishment, Report, p. 311; Minutes of Evidence, Aug. 5, 1949, p. 65.

29. Id., p. 267, par. 2281. Most American judges of course have no power to give such peremptory oral instructions.

30. Id., p. 372, par. 4501. See also the testimony of Viscount Simon to the same effect. Id., p. 380, par. 4600.

31. Id., p. 30, Appendix F.

32. Frank, *Law and the Modern Mind* (1930).

33. Pound, *Interpretations of Legal History,* p. 1 (1923).

34. "The rules and principles of case-law have never been treated as final truths but as working hypotheses, continually re-tested in those great laboratories of the law, the courts of justice. Every new case is an experiment; and if the accepted rule which seems applicable yields a result which is felt to be unjust, the rule is reconsidered." Monroe Smith, *Jurisprudence,* p. 21, (1909), quoted in Robinson, *Law and the Lawyers,* p. 280 (1935).

35. Frank, op. cit., supra, note 32, at p. 7.

36. Cardozo, *The Growth of the Law,* pp. 19-20 (1927).

37. Royal Commission, Report, p. 116.

38. American Law Institute, Proceedings of the 32d Annual Meeting, May 18-21, 1955, p. 206.

NOTES TO CHAPTER IV

1. Dr. D. Curran, testifying before the Royal Commission on Capital Punishment, Minutes of Evidence, p. 486, par. 6672 (1950). The Royal Medico-Psychological Association favored retention of the existing rules on similar reasoning:

"The Association is fully aware that, if the Rules were rigidly interpreted, the majority of even frankly insane murderers would be judged criminally responsible. But Lord Haldane said when Lord Chancellor, 'It is a great mistake to suppose that the Rules which absolve a person who does not know what he is doing and does not know the distinction between right and wrong, are hard and fast rules which cannot in any way be extended in their application.' (Parliamentary Debates, Vol. LVII, Fifth Series.) The Association is satisfied that in recent years there has been an increasing elasticity in the manner in which the rules have been interpreted and believes that justice is better served as the result." Id., p. 476 ¶11.

This and other testimony given before the Commission makes it "abundantly clear that the M'Naughten rules can be defended, even by their warmest supporters, as techniques whereby practical justice is reached, and not as absolute, precise rules." Morris, " 'Wrong' in the M'Naughten Rules," 16 *Modern L. Rev.* 435, 437 (1953).

2. Testimony before the Royal Commission on Capital Punishment. Quoted in Royal Commission Report, p. 102. See also the Commission's own statement: "But the fact that usually a way is found of obviating the evil consequences liable to flow from the Rules is not a sufficient reason for retaining them. The evil consequences are not always obviated. Occasionally the Rules lead to a verdict of 'guilty' and a sentence of death which might otherwise be avoided. Nor can we disregard the deplorable impression which the Rules make on the minds of persons interested in penal matters. The Rules bring the criminal law into disrepute and the doubts and anxieties they create in the minds of many critics are not removed by the consideration that the actual harm they do is much less than they are capable of doing." Ibid, p. 103.

3. *Durham* v. *United States,* 214 F. 2d 862 (1954).

4. The Commission's recommendation was for a change in the law which would "leave the jury to determine whether at the time

of the act the accused was suffering from disease of the mind (or mental deficiency) to such a degree that he ought not to be held responsible." Royal Commission, Report, pp. 116, 276.

5. American Law Institute, Model Penal Code, Tentative Draft No. 4, sec. 4.01 (1955).

6. Id., p. 158.

7. American Law Institute, Proceedings of the 32nd Annual Meeting, May 18-21, 1955, p. 217.

8. *R.* v. *Windle* [1952] 2 Q. B. 826; *Stapleton* v. *The Queen,* 86 Commonwealth Law Rep. 358 (Aust., 1952).

For a recent debate over whether "wrong" in the M'Naghten formula means legal or moral wrong, prompted by these two cases, see 16 *Modern Law Rev.* 435 (1953), and 17 id. 383 (1954).

9. *People* v. *Schmidt,* 216 N. Y. 324, 110 N. E. 2d 945 (1915). In a number of other cases, the courts have used the word "wrong" to mean both legal and moral wrong. See for example *People* v. *Sloper,* 198 Cal. 238, 244 Pac. 362 (1926); *State* v. *McGee,* 361 Mo. 309, 234 S. W. 2d 587 (1950); *Gibbs* v. *State,* 192 Tenn. 529, 241 S. W. 2d 556 (1951). The South Carolina court has said, "Under the law of this State, the test is mental capacity or the want of it sufficient to distinguish moral or legal right from moral or legal wrong, and to recognize the particular act charged as morally or legally wrong." *State* v. *Gardner,* 219 S. C. 97, 64 S. E. 2d 130 (1951).

It is not clear whether these cases mean that a defendant will be held responsible if he knew *either* that his act was morally wrong or that it was contrary to law, or whether they mean that he will not be held responsible unless he understood *both* that the act was morally wrong and illegal.

Some cases have said, in accordance with the English case of Windle, supra, that knowledge of the criminality of the act is sufficient to render a defendant responsible. *McElroy* v. *State,* 146 Tenn. 442, 242 S. W. 883 (1915); *Harrison* v. *State,* 44 Tax. Crim. 164, 69 S. W. 500 (1902).

10. The rule in Scotland is that a man may be "in a position to appreciate the nature and quality of his deed as an illegal act, which by the law of the country will be punished in a certain way, and may nevertheless be insane, his insanity consisting in a failure

to recognize that the act is morally wrong." *H. M. Advocate* v. *Sharp*, cited by Mr. C. C. Cunningham, Permanent Secretary, Scottish Home Dept., before the Royal Commission on Capital Punishment, Minutes of Evidence, pp. 77, 78, par. 581, 811.

11. Prof. Herbert Wechsler says ". . . I should think that if the defendant was psychotic and killed someone who either was or was believed to be persecuting him, the psychiatric examiner would probably conclude that the defendant's capacity to control the impulse to kill his persecutor, a capacity most normal people have, was at least substantially impaired." Letter to Dr. Guttmacher, reprinted in Model Penal Code, Tentative Draft No. 4, p. 189. But this lawyer's guess as to what psychiatrists would conclude is not concurred in by psychiatrist Guttmacher. Id., pp. 172, 187, 192.

12. Alabama, Arkansas, Colorado, Connecticut, Delaware, Illinois, Indiana, Kentucky, Massachusetts, Michigan, New Mexico, Utah, Vermont, Virginia, Wyoming, and perhaps also Montana and Ohio. For citations to cases see Weihofen, *Mental Disorder as a Criminal Defense*, p. 129 ff. (1954). The law of foreign countries whose penal codes provide that lack of volition under certain conditions may negative criminal responsibility is summarized in Keedy, "Irresistible Impulse as a Defense in the Criminal Law," 100 *U. Pa. L. Rev.* 956 (1952).

13. Waelder, "Psychiatry and the Problem of Criminal Responsibility," 101 *U. Pa. L. Rev.* 378, 383 (1954).

14. *United States* v. *Kunak*, 5 U. S. Ct. Mil. App. 346, 17 Court-Martial Rep. 346 (1954).
The facts of this case are sufficiently interesting to be worth stating in some detail. This young soldier became depressed after entering the army, and began thinking and talking about killing someone. Because he felt he was going to do something violent, he consulted the division psychiatrist, but received no comfort from him. He also consulted two chaplains. In an effort to get himself discharged, he had once stolen his company commander's boots. He told one officer that he had thought of punching the general in the nose so that he might be dishonorably discharged. He also had said that if he was not discharged he would shoot an officer and would blame the act on the major's failure to get him a discharge. The men he told of his impulse to kill only laughed at

him, called him "killer," and told him to commit suicide. Two or
three days prior to the homicide he had said that he was going to
kill one of the lieutenants.

On the day of the homicide, several officers and civilians were
seated at a lunch table when the accused approached carrying a
carbine. When he reached the table he executed a right face, lifted
the carbine and with the muzzle a few inches from the victim's
chest, shot one of the officers. The accused then lowered the carbine and stood at parade rest.

At his trial the evidence showed that he had quit high school
a few months before graduation because he was bothered and
worried. He had once jumped off a 75-foot bridge, and on another
occasion had ridden a motorcycle at a high rate of speed while
standing on his head. One of his four brothers was in a mental
institution and a sister had suffered a nervous breakdown.

He said that on the day of the homicide he was not thinking
"too much" about killing anyone; his loading the carbine was
"more or less mechanical." As he walked toward the officers' mess
he was thinking that "probably by this time next month I will be
dead." He was hoping someone would stop him; he knew he was
doing wrong but he could not do anything about it. After he
pulled the trigger he felt "flushed out."

The Government's three psychiatrists testified that on examination they had found the defendant free from mental disease or
defect and capable of distinguishing right from wrong and of
adhering to the right, although at least two of them regarded him
as emotionally unstable. Although the defense introduced no expert testimony of insanity, on review the case was referred to the
Surgeon General of the Army, for further inquiry into the issue of
sanity. On the information furnished, the Surgeon General's office
forwarded an opinion that defendant was sane at the time of the
act.

Subsequently, however, the board of review received a report
from the Disciplinary Barracks at Fort Leavenworth that the
accused had suffered two violent outbreaks while confined there.
A psychologist and a psychiatrist from the barracks informed the
board that in their opinion there was a reasonable doubt as to the
accused's present ability to adhere to the right, and they recommended further examination. He was thereupon further examined
by a board of medical officers at Fitzsimmons Hospital in Denver.
The Board found that while he was suffering from emotional

instability, he was sane at the time of the offense, at the time of trial, and at the time of their examination.

Thereafter, it was agreed to have still another examination, by a civilian psychiatrist, and Dr. Manfred Guttmacher of Baltimore was called into the case. He reported that in his opinion the accused was a paranoid schizophrenic, and that he was not a legally responsible agent at the time of the crime; that he was suffering from a psychotic irresistible impulse at the time of the crime and that he did not have a full appreciation of the wrongfulness of this act.

A criminal psychologist submitted an affidavit also agreeing with the diagnosis of paranoid schizophrenia. Thereupon the case was returned for redetermination of the issue of sanity. The board of review re-evaluated the testimony and the conflicting opinions of the experts, and again concluded that the evidence established that the accused was mentally responsible.

In Chapter III, the argument was discussed that the product rule would not give us a clear and definite test. It was pointed out that the right-and-wrong test is equally indefinite in its application. This case shows that the same is true of the irresistible-impulse test. Under army regulations, inability to "adhere to the right" is a defense. Was this defendant able to adhere to the right? He testified that he knew he was doing wrong but he could not do anything about it. Yet he also said that he would have stopped "if anyone had said something or did something, or stopped me."

To clarify its rule, the army at that time applied what is sometimes called the "policeman at the elbow" criterion: to come within the concept of inability to adhere to the right, the compulsion must have been "so strong that the act would have been committed even though a policeman had been at the accused's side at the time the opportunity to commit the offense presented itself." This has since been reworded in the new technical manual to read, "No impulse that can be resisted in the presence of a high risk of detection or apprehension is really very 'irresistible.' "

That is a very strict criterion, for as already said, very few persons are so disordered that they feel compelled to commit the crime even in the presence of a policeman. Yet even that does not dispose of this case, because this soldier in fact did commit the act in the very presence of several officers with power to arrest.

15. Royal Commission, Report, p. 110.

16. As already indicated (ante, note 14), the United States Court of Military Appeals has said that the phrase should be wholly omitted from instructions to a court-martial; the formulation used in courts-martial is "ability to distinguish right from wrong and to adhere to the right." See also *United States* v. *Dorothy K. Smith*, 5 U. S. Ct. Mil. App. 314, 17 C.M.R. 314 (1954).

The British Royal Commission on Capital Punishment similarly recommended that if the right-and-wrong test is to be retained— and not wholly discarded as a majority of the Commission felt should be done—at least it should be supplemented by requiring that the accused not only must have known that the act was wrong, but also that he "was incapable of preventing himself from committing it." A number of authorities who had testified before the Commission suggested other rewordings. Dr. Winfred Overholser suggested "incapable of . . . inhibiting his action in accordance with his understanding." Prof. Herbert Wechsler suggested "incapable of . . . acting in accordance with his knowledge [of what is right]." Royal Commission, Report, p. 111, par. 317, p. 116, par. 333; Id., Minutes of Evidence, p. 781, par. 16.

17. American Law Institute, Model Penal Code, Tentative Draft No. 4, p. 158.

18. Donald R. Cressey, "The Differential Association Theory and Compulsive Crimes," 45 *J. Crim. L. & Criminology* 29, 35 (1945).

19. E. H. Sutherland, *White Collar Crime* (1949).

20. Cressey, op. cit., p. 36.

21. Keedy, "Insanity and Criminal Responsibility," 30 *Harv. L. Rev.* 535 (1917); Keedy, "Criminal Responsibility of the Insane— A Reply to Professor Ballantine," 12 *J. Crim. L. & Criminology* 14 (1921); Keedy, "Tests of Criminal Responsibility," 1 *J. Crim. L. & Criminology* 394 (1910).

22. See Overholser and Weihofen, "Mental Disorder Affecting the Degree of a Crime," 56 *Yale L. J.* 959 (1947); Keedy, "A Problem of First Degree Murder: *Fisher* v. *United States*," 99 *U. Pa. L. Rev.* 267 (1950); Taylor, "Partial Insanity as Affecting the Degree of Crime—A Commentary on *Fisher* v. *United States*," 34 *Calif. L. Rev.* 625 (1946).

A good summary of the arguments in favor of recognizing

diminished responsibility is found in 41 Ky. L. J. 232 (1953). See also Report of the Royal Commission on Capital Punishment, p. 143, par. 411. Prof. Sheldon Glueck has suggested that the concept might be used in cases where a person suffering from mental disorder committed the crime during a so-called "lucid interval." Glueck, *Mental Disorder and the Criminal Law,* p. 374 (1925).

On the other hand, it has been objected that the concept would result in mentally disordered criminals being turned loose on society sooner than the sane and perhaps less dangerous offenders. Glanville Williams, *Criminal Law: The General Part,* p. 364 (1953). One answer to this criticism was provided by Lord Cooper, testifying before the Royal Commission. "In such cases," he pointed out, "there was machinery available by which he could be detained under a different statute if he were a dangerous lunatic." Royal Commission on Capital Punishment, Minutes of Evidence, April 4, 1950, p. 437, par. 5471.

Another objection that has been voiced is that the concept is too difficult for juries to apply. "Reduction in grade of offense usually means reducing first degree murder to second degree, and less frequently means reducing murder to manslaughter. In either event, it is achieved by relating the abnormal mental condition to malice, or premeditation, or deliberation, or similar state of mind. The abnormality, while insufficient to exculpate, is considered sufficient to negative the specific criminal state of mind. Therein lies the fallacy. Instead of being faced with the difficult task of relating abnormal mental condition to an exculpatory standard, the jury is asked to do that in addition to something even more difficult. This second difficulty is to relate an abnormal mental condition, short of the exculpatory standard, to an even finer and more delicate legal inquiry, namely, malice or premeditation." Polsky, "Applications and Limits of Diminished Responsibility as a Legal and Medical Concept," in Hoch and Zubin, *Psychiatry and the Law,* p. 196, at 211 (1955).

But Mr. Justice Murphy answered this argument in the Fisher case: ". . . juries constantly must judge the baffling psychological factors of deliberation and premeditation. . . . It seems senseless to shut the door on the assistance which medicine and psychiatry can give in regard to these matters, however inexact and incomplete that assistance may presently be. Precluding the consideration of mental deficiency only makes the jury's decision on deliberation and premeditation less intelligent and trustworthy."

Murphy, J., dissenting in *Fisher* v. *United States*, 328 U. S. 463, 493 (1946).

It has been suggested that adoption of the Durham case product rule might facilitate adoption of the concept of diminished responsibility. Note, 30 *Ind. L. J.* 194, at 215-16 (1955).

Scotland is unique among the English-speaking peoples in having developed a doctrine of diminished responsibility. The Scottish doctrine is not based on the Model Code rationale of mental disorder negativing the state of mind which is an essential element of the crime. The best statement of the Scottish doctrine is said to be the following, from the charge in the case of Braithwaite: "If he was suffering from some infirmity or aberration of mind or impairment of intellect to such an extent as not to be fully accountable for his actions, the result is to reduce the quality of his offense in a case like this from murder to culpable homicide." See Royal Commission Report, p. 77, par. 593. This seems (to an American legal mind) somewhat amorphous and even circular, for it seems to say only that he is not to be held fully accountable if he was not fully accountable. But all other statements of the rule seem to be equally loose. They seem to say merely that (1) there must be "some form of mental unsoundnss, or some aberration or weakness of mind," which (2) "is bordering on, though not amounting to, insanity;" and that (3) this condition so affected the mind "that responsibility is diminished from full responsibility to partial responsibility—in other words, the prisoner must be only partially accountable for his actions." Id., p. 394. Also Royal Commission, Minutes of Evidence, p. 453, par. 6064, 6066-6069.

The accused may plead "diminished responsibility," and on such a plea he has the burden of satisfying the jury that the balance of probability on the evidence is that his responsibility was below normal. If diminished responsibility is found, it may either (1) modify the character of the crime (as by reducing it from murder to culpable homicide), or (2) modify the sentence, or (3) both.

"The mental weakness, or weakness of responsibility, is regarded by our law as an extenuating circumstance, and it has the effect of modifying the character of the crime, or as justifying a modification of sentence, or both. When the jury has, under the presiding judge's direction, given effect to this extenuating circumstance by reducing the crime from murder to culpable homicide, the judge still has to consider whether it should have further weight when he is imposing sentence." *Kirkwood* v. *H. M. Advocate,* 1939 C. J. 36, reprinted in Royal Commission Report, p. 393.

Witnesses before the Royal Commission agreed that the Scottish doctrine works satisfactorily. Id. p. 133, par. 383. See Polsky, op. cit. Similar doctrines are found in several other countries. Royal Commission Report, pp. 413-416.

In others, it is included under a concept of extenuating circumstancess, e.g., in the Union of South Africa. Id. p. 482. But query whether this is not such a fundamental principle of responsibility that it should be defined as such, rather than that it be included in what must be left as a wide and vague group of "extenuating circumstances."

23. At this stage, I confess I am a little uncertain as to where the Institute and its Reporter stand on the value of certainty. The Reporter objected to the product rule because it was too broad and uncertain. But he was willing to submit the issue broadly to the jury's sense of justice. The Institute apparently thought that was too broad and uncertain. It rejected it, in favor of a rule which asks whether capacity is "substantially" impaired, and we are frankly told that "To identify the degree of impairment with precision is, of course, impossible both verbally and logically." American Law Institute, Model Penal Code, Tentative Draft No. 4, pp. 156, 159.

24. Dr. Gregory Zilboorg, in his *The Psychology of the Criminal Act and Punishment,* pp. 124-25 (1954), says of the concept of legal insanity: ". . . clinical psychiatry does not know of such a condition, never saw it, and after almost two hundred years of clinical investigations seriously doubts its existence."

25. American Law Institute, Model Penal Code, Tentative Draft No. 4, pp. 176-77.

26. Guttmacher and Weihofen, *Psychiatry and the Law,* p. 13 (1952).

27. Noce, Williams and Rapaport, "Reserpine (Serpasil) in the Management of the Mentally Ill and Mentally Retarded," 156 *J. Am. Med. Assn.* 821 (1954).

28. Edw. Podolsky, "The Chemical Brew of Criminal Behavior," 45 *J. Crim. L. & Criminology* 675, 677 (1955).

29. Id.

30. "Relatively good personality structure relates to normal EEG [electroencephalograph]. The more stable individuals among the prisoners, those convicted of single crimes, had only 17% abnormal EEG records . . . while those who were repeated offenders had 34% abnormal EEGs. . . ." Sol Levy and Margaret A. Kennard, "Study of the Electroencephalogram as Related to Personality Structure in a Group of Inmates of a State Penitentiary," quoted in Marcel Frym, "The Criminal Intent," 31 *Tex L. Rev.* 260, 267 (1953).

31. The late Lowell L. Selling said shortly before he died, "The whole concept of the law with regard to psychiatry probably will be changed within ten years, stemming from the fact that patients under indictment who have shock treatment do become entirely well before they can be brought to trial." 45 *J. Crim. L. & Criminology,* 719, 720 (1954).

32. John C. Whitehorn, "Psychiatry and Human Values," in Hoch and Zubin, *Psychiatry and the Law,* p. 144 at 145 (1955).

33. Gardner Murphy, "What Should be the Relation of Morals to Law? A Roundtable," 1 *J. Public L.* 313, 314 (1952).

34. Waelder, "Psychiatry and the Problem of Criminal Responsibility," 101 *U. Pa. L. Rev.* 378, 384 (1954).

35. Guttmacher, "The Psychiatrist as an Expert Witness," 22 *U. Chi. L. Rev.* 325, 328 (1955).

36. Tappan,"Medico-Legal Concepts of Criminal Insanity," 43 *J. Crim. L. & Criminology* 333 (1952); Tappan, "Some Myths about the Sex Offender," 19 *Fed. Probation* 7 (1955).

37. "The terms 'mental disease or defect' do not include an abnormality manifested only by repeated criminal or otherwise anti-social conduct." American Law Institute, Model Penal Code, sec. 4.01 (2).

This seems ineffectively worded in that psychopathy is rarely manifested *only* by criminal or antisocial behavior. Any defense lawyer will be able to avoid having his case come within this provision by introducing some additional evidence of mental disease or defect—and some additional evidence can always be found.

The Royal Commssion also concluded that, "For the present

we must accept the view that there is no qualitative distinction, but only a quantitative one, between the normal average individual and the psychopath, and the law must therefore continue to regard the psychopath as criminally responsible." It added, however, that "in many cases the responsibility of psychopaths can properly be regarded as diminished, and we think it would be right for the Secretary of State . . . to give rather greater weight to psychopathic personality as a ground for reprieve than has sometimes been the practice in the past." The Commission also endorsed the recommendation previously made by others, that a special institution be established to which both reprieved murderers and other psychopathic offenders could be sent, and where research into the problems of psychopathic personality could be pursued. Royal Commission, Report, pp. 139-40, par. 401, 402.

38. Sobeloff, "From McNaghten to Durham, and Beyond—A Discussion of Insanity and the Criminal Law," 41 *A.B.A.J.* 793, 878, reprinted in 15 *Md. L. Rev.* 93, 106-07 (1955).

39. See Dr. Guttmacher's comments, American Law Institute, Model Penal Code, Tentative Draft No. 4, p. 186.

40. "The true psychopath exists in a clinical group of his own, and can be the most dangerous, and in the absence of proper treatment, intractable criminal." Dr. E. Glover, testifying before the Royal Commission. Minutes of Evidence, p. 492, par. 20. It is Dr. Glover's opinion that, "Most crimes of violence are pathological, perhaps 70%." Id. p. 512, par. 6844, 6846. See also the Commission's Report, pp. 135-40, par. 393-401.

41. Roche, "Criminality and Mental Illness—Two Faces of the Same Coin," 22 *U. Chi. L. Rev.* 320, 322 (1955).

42. Guttmacher and Weihofen, *Psychiatry and the Law*, p. 458 (1952).

43. Roche, op. cit.

44. *United States* v. *Smith*, 5 U.S.C.M.R. 314, 17 C.M.R. 314, 324 (1954).

45. "It is rare for criminal conduct to be the first sign or indication of mental disorder. The mentally disordered criminal is a person who for years, or months, or weeks beforehand may have given evidence of his mental abnormality, and in numerous cases

medical advice may have been sought beforehand. When this is so, it introduces strong presumptive evidence of the *bona fides* of the case." Dr. D. Henderson, testifying before the Royal Commission, Minutes of Evidence, p. 460, ¶5.

Dr. Henry Yellowlees said that where a man suffering from a mental illness has committed a criminal act, "I do not think you can safely exclude in the case of an established mental disorder the probability that it had something to do with a criminal act." Id., p. 540, par. 7428.

The Royal Commission concluded: "Where a grave crime is committed by a person who is suffering from a psychosis and is so grossly disordered mentally that, in the opinion of experienced medical men, he could properly be certified as insane, the presumption that the crime was wholly or largely caused by the insanity is, in ordinary circumstances, overwhelmingly strong." Report, p. 101.

46. Group for the Advancement of Psychiatry, Committee on Psychiatry and Law, Criminal Responsibility and Psychiatric Expert Testimony (1954).

47. Mental disorder negativing criminal intent is made a defense by the Model Code. See ante, p. 73.

Deterrability as a test was considered by the Institute in one of the alternatives to sec. 4.01(1). This alternative read:

"(b) A person is not responsible for criminal conduct if at the time of such conduct as a result of mental disease or defect he lacks substantial capacity to appreciate the criminality of his conduct or is in such state that the prospect of conviction and punishment cannot constitute a significant restraining influence upon him."

The Institute's psychiatric advisers "considered the assessment of responsiveness to this one influence too difficult for psychiatric judgment." American Law Institute, Model Penal Code, Comments, p. 158. It was accordingly rejected. This seems sound. Psychiatrists have no methods for measuring the degree to which the prospect of punishment might restrain a given individual. Since the accused obviously has in fact *not* been restrained from committing an act by the prospect of punishment, it would seem difficult in any case to say that such prospect could constitute "a significant restraining influence upon him." It has been suggested that the question should be, not whether *this individual* is likely to be restrained by the prospect of punishment, but whether persons in his medical category could generally be so restrained. But this is still difficult to say, and raises the added problem of defining the "medical category."

48. Neustatter, *Psychological Disorder and Crime,* p. 12 (1953).

49. Royal Commission Report, p. 99.

50. Canadian psychiatrists, in a poll taken a few years ago, expressed themselves as favoring (63 out of 84) essentially the rule recommended by the Royal Commission—the presence of an actual psychosis or actual mental deficiency as the criterion for establishing legal irresponsibility. Stevenson, "Insanity as a Defence for Crime: Analysis of Replies," 25 *Can. Bar. Rev.* 871 (1947). See also Stevenson, Insanity as a Criminal Defence, Id. 731.

51. See 37 *Col. L. Rev.* 756 n. 92; *Tulane L. Rev.* 576, 580 (1955) See also Bishop, *New Criminal Law,* vol. 1, p. 231, sec. 383 (1892).

NOTES TO CHAPTER V

1. This chapter has appeared as an article in the Temple *Law Quarterly* (29 *Temple L.Q.* 235 [1956]). It is reprinted by permission of the editors of the *Quarterly.*

2. Twenty-three states hold that mental irresponsibility is an affirmative defense which the defendant has the burden of proving; about the same number of jurisdictions hold that the prosecution must prove sanity. See Weihofen, *Mental Disorder as a Criminal Defense,* pp. 212-272 (1954). Maryland in 1955, in a case of first impression, joined the states putting the burden of proof on the accused. *Thomas* v. *State,* 206 Md. 575, 112 A. 2d 913 (1955).

3. Royal Commission on Capital Punishment, 1949-1953, Report, p. 101, par. 286.

4. 10 Clark & Fin. 200 (1843).

5. Weihofen, op. cit., pp. 238-40.

6. Barry, "Insanity in the Criminal Law in Australia," 21 *Can. Bar Rev.* 429, 437 (1943). See also Barry, "The Defence of Insanity and the Burden of Proof," 2 *Res Judicatae* 42 (1939).

7. Wigmore, *Evidence,* p. 684 (1954).

8. Sec. 1.13(2).

9. Weihofen, op. cit., p. 227.

10. *Tatum* v. *United States,* 190 F. 2d 612 (1951); *Wright* v. *United States,* 215 F. 2d 498 (1954).

11. American Law Institute, Model Penal Code, Tentative Draft No. 4 (1955), Comments, p. 110.

12. American Law Institute, Proceedings, 1955, p. 225.

13. Guttmacher and Weihofen, *Psychiatry and the Law,* pp. 257-259 (1952); Weihofen, "Eliminating the Battle of Experts in Criminal Insanity Cases," 48 *Mich. L. Rev.* 961 (1950); Weihofen, "Trial or Execution of an Insane Defendant," 37 *Am. Bar Assn. J.* 651 (1951); Weihofen, "How Can We Eliminate the Battles of Medical Experts?" 39 *Neb. State Med. J.* 235 (1954).

14. American Law Institute, op. cit. supra, note 11, at p. 196, citing *Jessner* v. *State,* 202 Wis. 184, 231 N. W. 634 (1930).

15. Matter of Lutker, 000 Okla. Cr. 000, 274 P. 2d. 786 (1954).

16. *State* v. *Garrett,* order of Special Circuit Judge J. Russell McElroy, Nov. 24, 1955.

17. See *Higgins* v. *McGrath,* 98 F. Supp. 670 (1951); *Clements* v. *State,* 273 Ark. 460, 210 S. W. 2d 912 (1948); *People* v. *Supt. of Creedmoor State Hospital,* 40 N. Y. S. 2d 84, 91 (1943); *State* v. *Myers,* 220 S. C. 309, 67 S. E. 2d 506 (1951). See also *Sullivan* v. *Judges,* 271 Mass. 435, 171 N. E. 490 (1930); *Cogburn* v. *State,* 000 Tenn. 000, 281 S. W. 2d 28 (1955).

18. *Comm.* v. *Patskin,* 375 Pa. 368, 100 A. 2d 472, 473 n. (1953).

19. Weihofen, op. cit., supra n. 2 at p. 446.

20. Id., p. 458.

21. *Gunther* v. *United States,* 215 F. 2d 493 (1954); *Contee* v. *United States,* 215 F. 2d 324 (1954).

22. Report of the Committee on Mental Disorder as a Criminal Defense, to the Council on Law Enforcement of the District of

Columbia, Ap. 25, 1955, p. 23. The local statute has since been amended to accept this recommendation. Pub. L. No. 313, 84th Cong., 1st Session §1(b) (Aug. 9, 1955), amending D. C. Code Ann. §24-301 (1951).

23. *State* v. *Eisenstein,* 72 Ariz. 320, 235, P. 2d 1011 (1951); *Comm.* v. *Russo,* 232 Mass. 58, 122 N. E. 176 (1919); *State* v. *Privitt,* 175 Mo. 207, 75 S. W. 457 (1903); *Tvrz* v. *State,* 154 Neb. 641, 48 N. W. 2d 761 (1951); *State* v. *Hayden,* 51 Vt. 296 (1878); *State* v. *Spangler,* 92 Wash. 636, 159 Pac. 810 (1916); *State* v. *Eggleston,* 161 Wash. 486, 297 Pac. 162 (1931); *Cornell* v. *State,* 104 Wis. 527, 80 N. W. 745 (1899); *State* v. *Carroll,* 52 Wyo. 29, 69 P. 2d 542 (1937). Professor McCormick says that in Maryland, Missouri, Minnesota, Pennsylvania and Wisconsin, it is usual to ask an expert who has heard all the evidence in the trial to state an opinion of the defendant's sanity, based on the evidence. McCormick, "Direct Examination of Medical Experts in Actions for Death and Bodily Injuries," 12 *La. L. Rev.* 264, 271 (1952).

More than a century ago, Dr. Isaac Ray inveighed against the legal rule permitting a physician to testify to an opinion as to mental condition based merely upon observation in court: "If a physician, after listening to divers vague and rambling details concerning a person's ill-health, and looking at him across the apartment, without being permitted to address to him a single word, or lay a finger on his person, should then be required to say on his oath, whether or not the individual in question were laboring under inflammation of the lungs, bowels, or kidneys, he would scarcely restrain a smile at the stupidity which should expect a satisfactory answer." Ray, *Medical Jurisprudence of Insanity,* p. 64, sec. 44 (3d ed. 1855).

24. The abolition of the hypothetical question has been urged not only by medical groups such as the American Psychiatric Association, but also by legal writers such as Wigmore and McCormick.. Menninger, "Medico-Legal Recommendations of the American Psychiatric Association," 19 *J. Crim. L. & Criminology,* 367, 376 (1928); Wigmore, *Evidence,* sec. 686 (3d ed. 1940); McCormick, Some Observations Upon the Opinion Rule and Expert Testimony, 23 *Tex. L. Rev.* 109 (1945).

On the other hand, Dr. Henry A. Davidson has urged retention of the hypothetical question. "This keeps the psychiatrist honest, because he can shape his answer to fit the hypothesis and let the lawyers settle among themselves which hypothesis is correct.

". . . the hypothetical question is a boon and psychiatrists should resist any effort to get rid of it." Davidson, "Psychiatrists in Administration of Criminal Justice," 45 *J. Crim. L. & Criminology* 12, 16-17 (1954). See also Francis X. Busch, "The Hypothetical Question," 3 *J. Public L.* 550, 558 (1954) ("Despite the judicial criticism leveled at the hypothetical question, it has in many cases definite probative and persuasive value which should prompt its use where indicated").

25. Royal Commission on Capital Punishment, Minutes of Evidence, p. 516, ¶6964.

26. "Of the courts that have passed on the issue, at least ten have held that mental disease, not sufficient to relieve from responsibility entirely, should still be considered in determining whether the requirements of deliberation and premeditation needed for the first degree murder have been met (California, Colorado, Connecticut, Indiana, Ohio, Rhode Island, Tennessee, Utah, Virginia, Wisconsin, and perhaps also Kentucky, Montana and Oregon). Maryland and New York in dicta have also approved the rule. It has been rejected in Arizona, Idaho, and Missouri, and perhaps also in the District of Columbia, Massachusetts, Nevada, and Pennsylvania, although it is possible to distinguish most of the cases from these jurisdictions. In New Jersey, the cases leave the law unclear." Weihofen, op. cit. pp. 183-85 (citing cases). See also Keedy, "A Problem of First Degree Murder: Fisher v. United States," 99 *U. Pa. L. Rev.* 267 (1950); Taylor, "Partial Insanity as Affecting the Degree of Crime — A Commentary on Fisher v. United States," 34 *Calf. L. Rev.* 625 (1946); Weihofen and Overholser, "Mental Disorder Affecting the Degree of a Crime," 56 *Yale L. J.* 959 (1947).

27. *People* v. *Wells,* 33 Cal. 2d 330, 202 P. 2d 53 (1949); *People* v. *Leick,* 000 Colo. 000, 281 P. 2d 806 (1955).

28. See *People* v. *Troche,* 206 Cal. 35, 273 Pac. 767 (1928); *People* v. *French,* 12 Cal. 2d 720, 87 P. 2d 1014 (1939); *People* v. *Cordova,* 14 Cal. 2d 308, 94 P. 2d 40 (1939); *People* v. *Wells,* supra; *People* v. *Nichols,* 88 Cal. A. 2d 221, 198 P. 2d 538 (1948); Comment, 24 *Ry. Mt. L. Rev.* 223 (1952).

29. See *Draper* v. *Denno*, 113 F. Supp. 290, aff'd., 205 F. 2d 570 (1953); *State* v. *Eisenstein*, 72 Ariz. 320, 235 P. 2d 1011; *State* v. *Daley*, 54 Ore. 514, 103 Pac. 502, 104 Pac. 1 (1909).

30. *Taylor* v. *United States*, 222 F. 2d 398 (1955).

31. Sheldon Glueck, *Crime and Correction: Selected Papers*, p. 159 (1952).

32. *Taylor* v. *United States*, 222 F. 2d 398 (1955).

33. See Guttmacher and Weihofen, *Psychiatry and the Law*, ch. 12 (1952); Guttmacher and Weihofen, "Privileged Communications between Psychiatrist and Patient," 28 *Ind. L. J.* 32 (1952); Diamond and Weihofen, "Privileged Communication and the Clinical Psychologist," 9 *J. of Clinical Psychology* 388 (1953); Weihofen, "Eliminating the Battle of Experts," 1 *Nat. Probation and Parole Assn. J.* 105 (1955).

34. For examples of "wide inequality and vast disparity" in sentences imposed by different federal judges, see McGuire and Holtzoff, "The Problem of Sentence in the Criminal Law," 20 *Boston U. L. Rev.* 423 (1940).

35. Barnes, Essentials of a Rational Approach to the Crime Problem, in Crimes of Violence, the Report of a Conference on Crime Sponsored by the University of Colorado, Aug. 15-18, 1949, pp. 5-6.

36. Bromberg and Cleckley, "The Medico-Legal Dilemma: A Suggested Solution," 42 *J. Crim L. & Criminology* 729 (1952); Bernard Glueck, "Report of the Ninth International Prison Congress" (1926), *Mental Hygiene*, No. 1; Menninger, "Medico-Legal Proposals of the American Psychiatric Association," 19 *J. Crim. L. & Criminology* 367, 373 (1928); Smith, "Scientific Proof and Relations of Law and Medicine," 21 *Can. Bar Rev.* 707, 717 (1943). Some eminent legal writers have also endorsed such proposals. Sheldon Glueck, *Mental Disorder and the Criminal Law*, pp. 31, n. 1, 461 ff. (1925); Stallybrass, *The Modern Approach to Criminal Law*, p. 418 (1945); Gausewitz, "Considerations Basic to a New Penal Code," 11 *Wis. L. Rev.* 346 (1936); Sheldon Glueck, "Principles of a Rational Penal Code," 41 *Harv. L. Rev.* 453 (1928); Harno, "Rationale of a Criminal Code," 85 *U. Pa. L. Rev.* 549 (1937). See also, Bergan, "The Sentencing Power in Criminal Cases," 13 *Albany L. Rev.* 1 (1949).

37. See *State* v. *Lange,* 168 La. 958, 123 So. 639 (1929); *Sinclair* v. *State,* 161 Miss. 142, 132 So. 581 (1931); *State* v. *Strasburg,* 60 Wash. 106, 110 Pac. 1020 (1910); Rood, "Statutory Abolition of the Defense of Insanity in Criminal Cases," 9 *Mich. L. Rev.* 126 (1910).

38. Guttmacher and Weihofen, *Psychiatry and the Law,* p. 446 (1952).

39. See for example the more recent type of statutes dealing with sex offenders. Mich. Pub. Acts 1952, no. 58, p. 63; N. J. Rev. Stat. (Cum. Supp. 1950) tit. 2, ch. 192, sec. 1.13 et seq.; N. Y. Laws 1950, Ch. 525; Pa. Stat. (Purdon) tit. 19, secs. 1166-1174, added by Pa. Laws 1952, Act 495. See Guttmacher and Weihofen, "Sex Offenses," 43 *J. Crim. L. & Criminology* 153, 168-171 (1952). In Great Britain and in Scotland, it has also been recommended that the advice of a medical expert be obtained before a person convicted of a sex offense is sentenced, in reports of a joint committee of the British Medical Association and the Magistrates' Association, and of the Scottish Advisory Council on the Treatment and Rehabilitation of Offenders.

40. A. B. A. Reports, 1929, vol. 54, p. 56.

41. Sheldon Glueck, "Pre-Sentence Examination of Offenders to Aid in Choosing a Method of Treatment," 41 *J. Crim. L. & Criminology* 717, 730 (1951), reprinted in Glueck, *Crime and Correction: Selected Papers,* 102, 117-18 (1952).

NOTES TO CHAPTER VI

1. See, for examples of such judicial prophecies of doom, *State* v. *Buck,* 205 Iowa 1028, 219 N. W. 17 (1928); *Smith* v. *State,* 95 Miss. 768, 49 So. 836 (1909); *State* v. *Williamson,* 106 Mo. 173, 17 S. W. 172 (1891); *Oborn* v. *State,* 143 Wis. 249, 126 N. W. 737 (1910).

2. Washington (D. C.) *Evening Star,* Oct. 7, 1954, p. A-24, col. 1.

3. Letter to the author from Mr. George L. Hart, Jr., Oct. 3, 1955.

4. "Dr. William Alanson White made a study many years ago showing that, on the average, perpetrators of homicide committed

to institutions for the insane spent more time in confinement than those sentenced to penal institutions." Sobeloff, "From McNaghten to Durham, and Beyond—A Discussion of Insanity and the Criminal Law," 41 *Am. Bar Assn. J.* 793, 878, reprinted in 15 *Md. L. Rev.* 93, 108 (1955).

5. Ray, *Medical Jurisprudence of Insanity,* p. 349, sec. 341 (3d ed. 1855).

6. See Alexander and Staub, *The Criminal, The Judge and The Public,* p. 207 et seq. (Zilboorg trans., 1931).

7. Wechsler, "The Criteria of Criminal Responsibility," 22 *U. Chi. L. Rev.* 367, 374-75 (1955).

8. Dession, "Justice After Conviction," 25 *Conn. Bar. J.* 215, 221-22 (1951).

9. Holmes, *The Common Law,* p. 41 (1881).

10. Stephen, *History of the Criminal Law of England,* vol. 2, pp. 81-82 (1883).

11. Frym, "Past and Future of Criminal Rehabilitation," 3 *J. Public Law* 451, 460 (1955).

12. Testimony before the Royal Commission on Capital Punishment, Minutes of Evidence, p. 338, par. 4128 (1950).

13. See Neustatter, *Psychological Disorder and Crime,* p. 223 (1953).

14. Glanville Williams, "The Royal Commission and the Defence of Insanity," in 7 *Current Legal Problems* 16, 25 (1954).

15. Boudreau, "Mental Health, The New Public Health Frontier," 286 *Annals of the Am. Academy of Pol. and Soc. Science* 1, 4 (March, 1953).

16. Carter, *Law: Its Origin, Growth and Function,* p. 217 (1907).

17. Warren, *The Supreme Court in United States History,* pp. 608, 616-18 (rev. ed. 1926).

18. It is sometimes argued that our long prison sentences must be viewed in light of the fact that person may be paroled before full term is served. That is true, but most other countries also

have parole or provisions for earlier release, pardon, etc. In
Sweden a limited number, including murderers, are actually
allowed to go out and earn ordinary wages in the market outside
the prisons.

19. Deets, "Changes in Capital Punishment Policy Since 1939,"
38 *J. Crim. L. & Criminology* 584 (1948); Hartung, "Trends in
the Use of Capital Punishment," 284 *Annals of the Am. Academy
of Pol. & Soc. Science,* p. 8 (1952); Viscount Samuel, testimony
before the Royal Commission on Capital Punishment, Minutes
of Evidence, Mar. 3, 1950, p. 380 (1950).

20. Hartung, op. cit. at p. 14; Vold, "Extent and Trend of Capital
Crimes in the United States," 284 *Annals* 1, 3 (1952).

21. Sellin, Memorandum submitted to the Royal Commission
on Capital Punishment, Minutes of Evidence, Feb. 1, 1951, p.
656.

22. Vold, op. cit., p. 4.

23. "Even in personality studies of murderers it is rare to find
any mention of the role which the potential threat of execution
is assumed to play. It is only those who are primarily concerned
with the social policy of penal treatment who in considering the
death penalty wonder what purpose it may serve. The behavior
scientist has apparently written off this problem as of no significance. He has found that murder is a type of conduct which
at least in well-ordered countries is as irrational as the penalty
which threatens it." Sellin, op. cit. ante note 21, at par. 84.

24. Testimony of Warden Hugh Christie of Okalla Prison Farm,
South Burnaby, British Columbia, before the Committee on
Capital and Corporal Punishment and Lotteries (Canada), Min-
utes of Proceedings and Evidence, No. 14, May 18, 1954, p. 590.

25. "Psychoanalytic theory sees both suicide and homicide as
extreme forms of aggression, the one directed against the self, the
other directed against another person. Suicide is seen as a function of an aggressively strict and punishing 'superego' or inter-
nalizing restraining mechanism of the personality which prohibits
the outward expression of aggression." Andrew F. Henry and
James F. Short, Jr., *Suicide and Homicide,* p. 13 (1954). There
are about twice as many suicides in the United States as murders.

Id. In England in 1946-48, aside from cases of infanticide, of 301 known murderers, 35 percent actually committed suicide before arrest. This suggests that the suicidal tendency is strong in murderers. Royal Commission on Capital Punishment, Minutes of Evidence, p. 532-3, par. 4646, testimony of Dr. William H. Gillespie of the Institute of Psycho-Analysis.

26. Whelan, "An Experiment in Predicting Deliquency," 45 *J. Crim. L. & Criminology* 432 (1954).

27. Testimony of Dr. J. S. Hopwood, Med. Supt. of Broadmoor Institution, before the Royal Commission, Minutes of Evidence, pp. 359, 361 par. 4344, 7406 (1950). See also testimony of Dr. Gillespie, Id., p. 553, par. 7646.

28. Bernard C. Glueck, Jr., "Changing Concepts in Forensic Psychiatry," 45 *J. Crim. L. & Criminology* 123, 130-31 (1954). See also Edw. Podolsky, "Mind of the Murderer," 45 *J. Crim. L. & Criminology* 48 (1954).

29. "England had 17 capital crimes in the early part of the fifteenth century. This number was rapidly increased about the first quarter of the seventeenth century, reaching a peak, according to Radzinowicz, of some 350 capital crimes by 1780! Practically all the capital crimes added after 1500 were offenses against property, most of these crimes being trivial. This number was drastically reduced in the nineteenth century: to about 220 by 1825, to about 17 in 1839 and to 4 in 1861. This number was further reduced by the time capital punishment was suspended by the Parliament in 1948 [for a trial period]." Hartung, op. cit. ante, note 19, at p. 11.

30. "The Abolition of Capital Punishment: A Symposium," 32 *Can. Bar Rev.* 485, 492 (1954); Calvert, *Capital Punishment in the Twentieth Century*, p. 7 (1927).

31. Testimony before the Royal Commission on Capital Punishment, Minutes of Evidence, p. 582, par. 7990 (1950).

32. "The Abolition of Capital Punishment: A Symposium," 32 *Can. Bar Rev.* 485, 495 (1954).

33. Vold, "Extent and Trend of Capital Crimes in the United States," 284 *Annals of the Am. Academy of Pol. and Soc. Science.* 1, 4 (Nov. 1952); Schuessler, "The Deterrent Influence of the Death Penalty," id., p. 54, 58.

34. Glover, "Psychiatric Aspects of the Report on Capital Punishment," 17 *Modern L. Rev.* 329, 330 (1954).

35. Royal Commission on Capital Punishment, Report, p. 335.

36. See Joint Committee of the Senate and House of Commons on Capital and Corporal Punishment and Lotteries (Canada), Appendix "F" of the Minutes of Proceedings and Evidence No. 20 (1955), "Findings of U. S. A. Surveys on the Death Penalty and Police Safety," by Prof. Thorsten Sellin and Donald Campion, S.J.

37. Quoted in 32 *Can. Bar Rev.* 485 at 499 (1954).

38. Hartung, op. cit. ante, note 19, at pp. 17-18.

39. Testimony before the Royal Commission on Capital Punishment, Minutes of Evidence, pp. 551, 553-54, par. 7624, 7664, (1950).

40. Quoted in Ehrmann, "The Death Penalty and the Administration of Justice," 284 *Annals of the Am. Academy of Pol. and Soc. Science* 73, at pp. 82-3n (Nov. 1952).

41. Hartung, op. cit. p. 11.

42. Vt. Rev. Stat. (1947) § 8242; See also D. C. Code (1951) § 22-2404. See Knowlton, "Problems of Jury Discretion in Capital Cases," 101 *U. Pa. L. Rev.* 1099 (1953).

43. There can of course be no statistics on the number of murders actually committed. As a matter of fact there are not even general statistics available as to the number of persons convicted per year of first degree murder. But in 1951, there were 6,820 cases of "murder and non-negligent manslaughter" known to the police. But only about 1600 to 1800 persons are sent to prison each year for murder, and, as said, only about 100 are executed. See Vold, op. cit. ante note 33, at p. 6; Hartung, op. cit. ante note 19, at p. 13.

44. Royal Commission on Capital Punishment, Minutes of Evidence, Mar. 2, 1950, p. 351, par. 4209.

45. "An average of one execution a year in a state of two million hardly suggests a constructive use of a rational instrument of penal policy unless we assume a selective process of incredible sensitivity and a subject who so far exceeds familiar ranges of

pathological malformation, of dangerousness and of incorrigibility as to fall quite outside the human species." Dession, "Justice After Conviction," 25 *Conn. Bar J.* 215, 225 (1951).

Prof. Thorsten Sellin has said that the controversy over the death penalty is out of all proportion to its frequency of application. It is in fact "the rarest of all severe criminal punishments." Sellin, Memorandum submitted to the Royal Commission on Capital Punishment, Minutes of Evidence, Feb. 1, 1951, p. 647. That is why it is not a deterrent and "probably can never be made a deterrent. Its very life seems to depend on its rarity and, therefore, on its ineffectiveness as a deterrent." Sellin, "Common Sense and the Death Penalty," *Prison J.,* vol. 12, no. 4, p. 12 (Oct. 1932).

46. Lawes, *Twenty Thousand Years in Sing Sing,* p. 302 (1932).

47. Hartung, op. cit.

48. House of Representatives, 69th Cong., first sess., Report No. 876, sp. 14, 1926.

49. Lawes, op. cit., at p. 336.

50. A. M. Kirkpatrick, exec. dir., John Harvard Society of Ontario, before the Joint Committee on Capital and Corporal Punishment and Lotteries (Canada), Min. of Proceedings and Evidence No. 14, May 19, 1954, p. 607.

51. Testimony before the Royal Commission on Capital Punishment, Minutes of Evidence, p. 580, par. 7967 (1950).

52. Viscount Templewood, testifying before the Royal Commission. Id., p. 629, par. 8556.

53. Gehman, *A Murder in Paradise,* pp. 3, 4, 6 (1954).

54. "After 1931 about half the states in the Union introduced the death penalty for kidnapping for ransom, and the Federal Government also introduced the death penalty for that crime. . . . The first execution did not occur until years after the 'market' disappeared. I suspect that the reason why kidnapping for ransom disappeared as a behaviour was that all the machinery of law enforcement, from the Federal Bureau of Investigation down to the local policeman, was focused on its prevention. This was a business crime, and when the market disappeared, it was no longer

a profitable venture. We saw the same thing happen in connection with automobile theft during the depression. While other thefts of various kinds increased, automobile thefts dropped during the depression to a very low degree. The stealing of automobiles for sale and exportation disappeared, because the buyer disappeared. . . . If a government were to apply similarly preventive methods to certain other types of criminality, they, too, would show a reduction. I do not think that murder ordinarily falls in that category. The psychological character of the crime is such that it would probably have no effect. Gang murders would, of course, disappear with the disappearance of gangs. Gangs could be broken up and made to disappear by effective police action, suported by the community, as anyone who knows anything about local conditions in the United States realizes." Prof. Thorsten Sellin, testifying before the Royal Commission on Capital Punishment, Minutes of Evidence, p. 673, par. 8885 (1951).

55. The Diagnostic Center at Menlo Park, New Jersey, is an outstanding experiment in studying "problem children." A staff of specially trained psychiatrists, neurologists, clinical psychologists and social workers makes a thorough organic examination of the child. Standardized psychological and psychometric tests, interviews under sodium pentathol and projective creative art tests are also used. After a 90-day study, an extensive report is prepared, offering not only a diagnosis but also specific recommendations for future treatment and management of the delinquent. Frym, "Past and Future of Criminal Rehabilitation," 3 *J. Public L.* 451, 455 (1954).

The New York City Youth Board has been experimenting with the Glueck prediction techniques in two selected public schools in the Bronx, to see if they will make it possible to detect those first grade children who are likely to become delinquent later. At the same time, the board is also conducting experiments in delinquency treatment to test whether they are effective in preventing delinquency from developing in those children for whom delinquency is predicted by the Glueck techniques. Whelan, "An Experiment in Predicting Delinquency," 45 *J. Crim L. & Criminology* 432 (1954).

The Patuxent Institution in Maryland, which opened in 1955, is also engaged in an interesting experimental program for the treatment of "defective delinquents."

Index